4-Chord Songbook

Bob Marley

WISE PUBLICATIONS
part of The Music Sales Group
London / New York / Paris / Sydney / Copenhagen / Berlin / Madrid / Tokyo

This *4-Chord Songbook* allows even beginner guitarists to play and enjoy classic hits. With the same 4 chords used throughout the book, you'll soon master your favourite Bob Marley songs.

The *4-Chord Songbook* doesn't use music notation. Throughout the book chord boxes are printed at the head of each song; the chord changes are shown above the lyrics. It's left to you, the guitarist, to decide on a strum pattern or picking pattern.

You might find that the pitch of the vocal line is not always comfortable because it is pitched too high or too low. In that case, you can change the key without learning a new set of chords; simply place a capo behind a suitable fret.

Whatever you do, this *4-Chord Songbook* guarantees hours of enjoyment for guitarists of all levels, as well as providing a fine basis for building a strong repertoire.

Published by
Wise Publications
14-15 Berners Street, London W1T 3LJ, UK.

Exclusive Distributors:
Music Sales Limited
Distribution Centre, Newmarket Road, Bury St Edmunds, Suffolk IP33 3YB, UK.
Music Sales Pty Limited
120 Rothschild Avenue, Rosebery, NSW 2018, Australia.

Order No. AM988196
ISBN 1-84609-821-1

Printed in the EU.

www.musicsales.com

Africa Unite

Words & Music by
Bob Marley

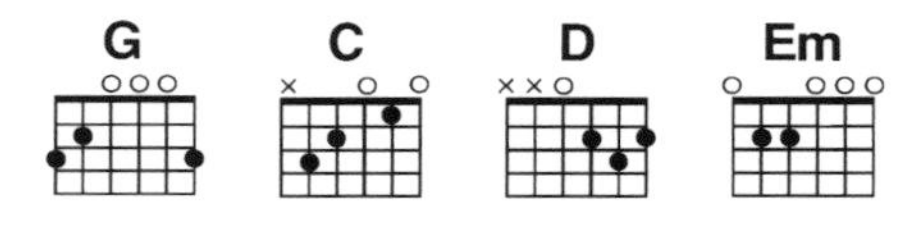

Intro ‖: G D | Em | G D | Em :‖

Chorus 1

G D Em
Africa, unite,
C D Em
'Cause we're moving right out of Babylon
C D Em
And we're going to our father's land.

Verse 1

G D
How good and how pleasant it would be
Em C
Before God and man, yeah,
G D Em C
To see the unification of all Africans, yeah.
G D Em C
As it's been said already let it be done, yeah.
G D Em C
We are the children of the Rastaman,
G D Em C
We are the children of the Higher Man.

Chorus 2

G D Em
Africa, unite,
G D Em
'Cause the children wanna come home.
G D Em
Africa, unite,
C D Em
'Cause we're moving right out of Babylon
C D Em
And we're grooving to our father's land.

Verse 2

G D
How good and how pleasant it would be
Em C
Before God and Man,
G D Em C
To see the unification of all Rastaman, yeah.
G D Em C
As it's been said already, let it be done.
G D Em C
I tell you who we are under the sun:
G D Em C
We are the children of the Rastaman,
G D Em C
We are the children of the Higher Man.

Chorus 3

G D Em
So, Africa unite,
G D Em
Afri-Africa unite,
G D Em
Unite for the benefit of your people,
G D Em
Unite for it's later than you think,
G D Em
Unite for the benefit of your children,
G D Em
Unite for it's later than you think.
G D Em
Africa awaits its creators,
G D Em
Africa awaiting its creators.
G D Em
Africa, you're my forefathers' cornerstone.
G D Em
Unite for the Africans abroad. *To Fade*

Baby We've Got A Date (Rock It Baby)

Words & Music by
Bob Marley

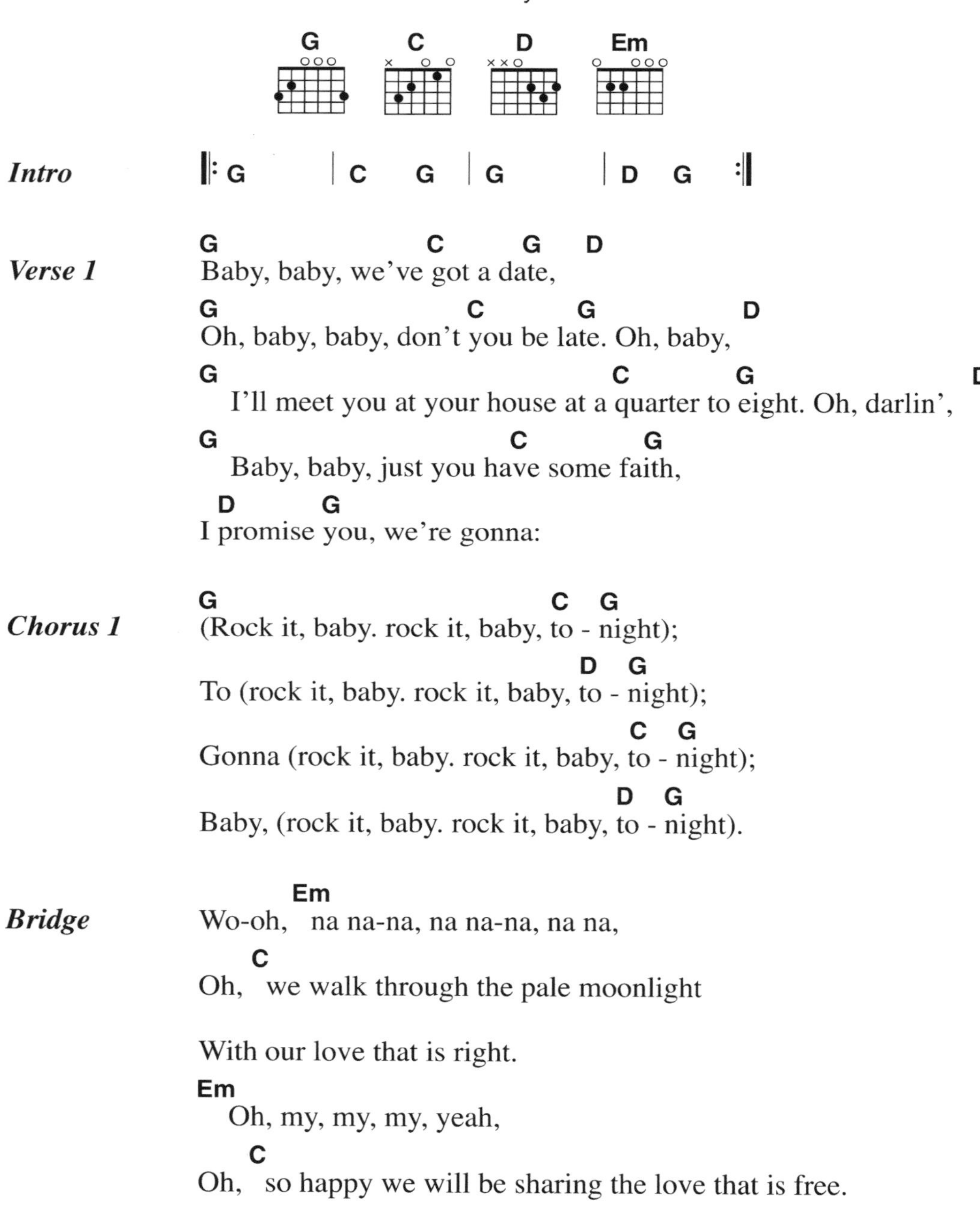

Intro | G | C G | G | D G :|

Verse 1

G C G D
Baby, baby, we've got a date,
G C G D
Oh, baby, baby, don't you be late. Oh, baby,
G C G D
I'll meet you at your house at a quarter to eight. Oh, darlin',
G C G
Baby, baby, just you have some faith,
D G
I promise you, we're gonna:

Chorus 1

G C G
(Rock it, baby. rock it, baby, to - night);
D G
To (rock it, baby. rock it, baby, to - night);
C G
Gonna (rock it, baby. rock it, baby, to - night);
D G
Baby, (rock it, baby. rock it, baby, to - night).

Bridge

Em
Wo-oh, na na-na, na na-na, na na,
C
Oh, we walk through the pale moonlight

With our love that is right.
Em
Oh, my, my, my, yeah,
C
Oh, so happy we will be sharing the love that is free.

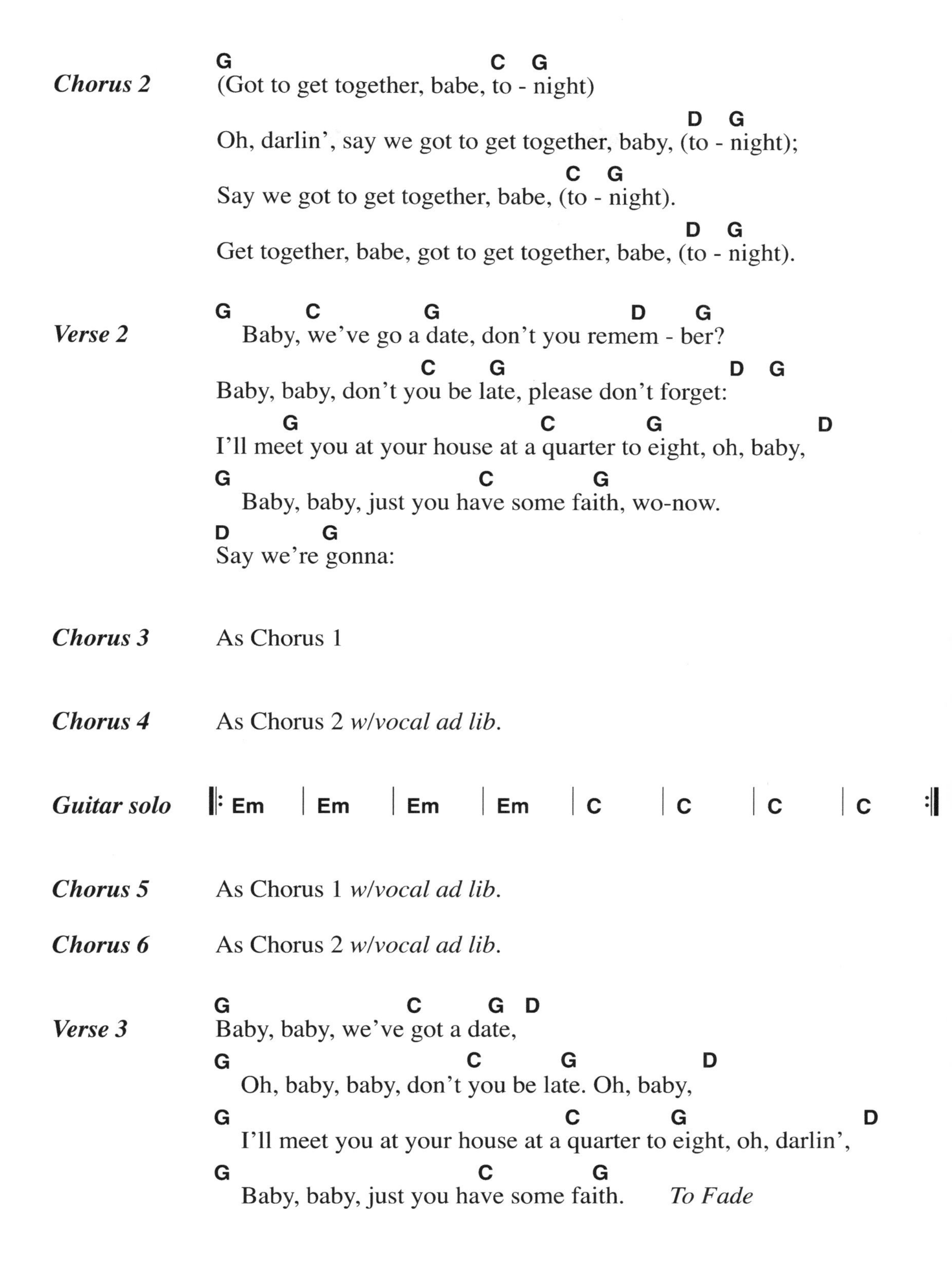

Chorus 2

```
G                               C  G
(Got to get together, babe, to - night)
                                            D   G
Oh, darlin', say we got to get together, baby, (to - night);
                                 C  G
Say we got to get together, babe, (to - night).
                                            D   G
Get together, babe, got to get together, babe, (to - night).
```

Verse 2

```
G       C         G                     D    G
   Baby, we've go a date, don't you remem - ber?
                   C    G                      D   G
Baby, baby, don't you be late, please don't forget:
       G                              C       G            D
I'll meet you at your house at a quarter to eight, oh, baby,
G                             C       G
   Baby, baby, just you have some faith, wo-now.
D        G
Say we're gonna:
```

Chorus 3 As Chorus 1

Chorus 4 As Chorus 2 *w/vocal ad lib.*

Guitar solo 𝄆 Em | Em | Em | Em | C | C | C | C 𝄇

Chorus 5 As Chorus 1 *w/vocal ad lib.*

Chorus 6 As Chorus 2 *w/vocal ad lib.*

Verse 3

```
G                    C    G  D
Baby, baby, we've got a date,
G                          C       G          D
   Oh, baby, baby, don't you be late. Oh, baby,
G                                    C      G              D
   I'll meet you at your house at a quarter to eight, oh, darlin',
G                             C      G
   Baby, baby, just you have some faith.      To Fade
```

Bend Down Low

Words & Music by
Bob Marley

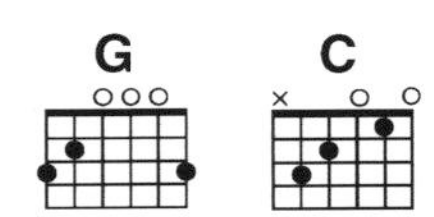

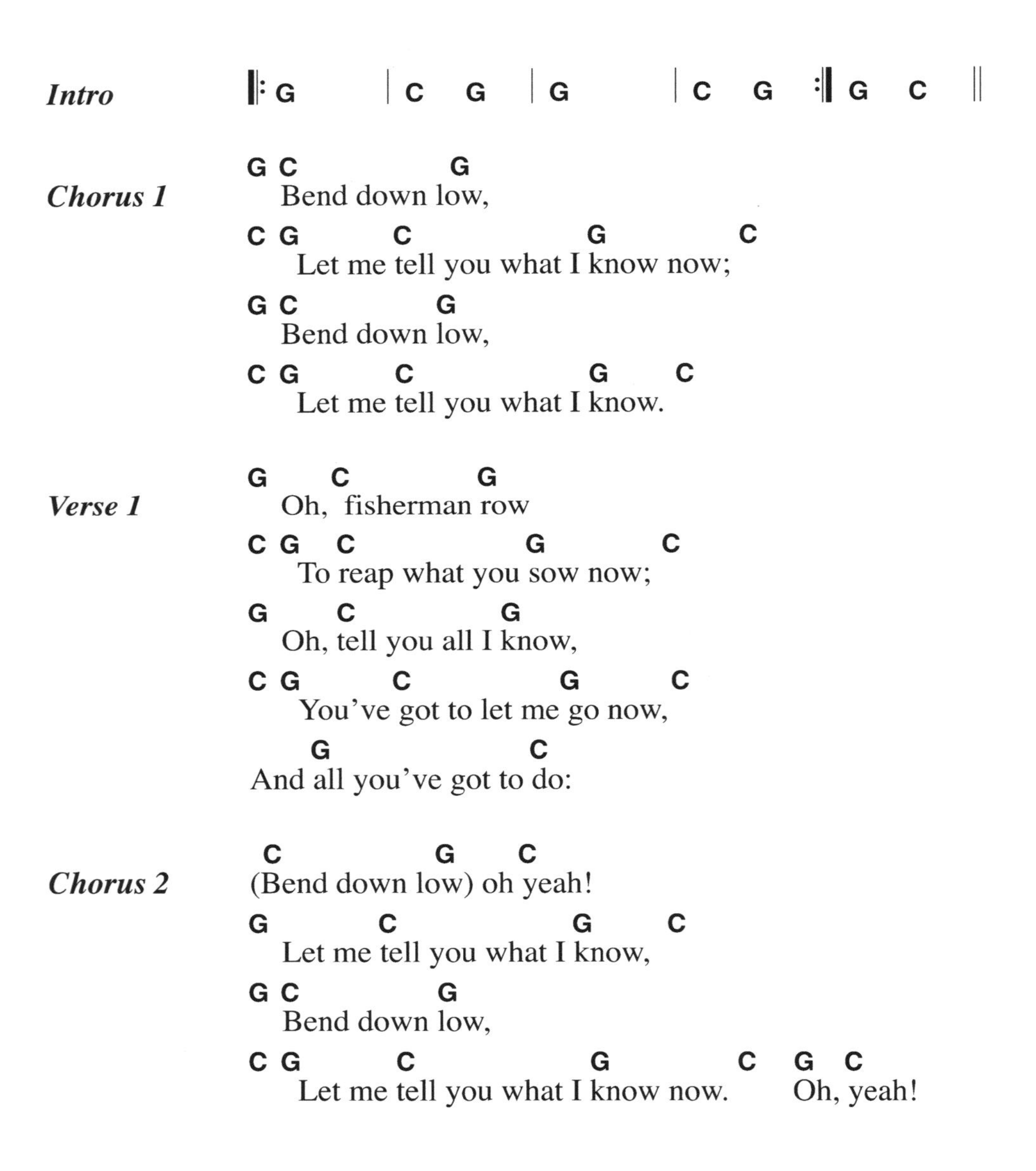

Verse 2

G C G C
Keep on knocking, but you can't come in.
G C G C
I get to understand you been living in sin,
G C G C
But if you love me, woman, walk right in.
G C G C
I've got a notch for your safety-pin,

But bend down low.

Instrumental

|: G C | G C | G C | G C :|
(low).

Verse 3

G C G C
Keep on knocking, but you can't come in.
G C G C
I get to understand you been living in sin,
G C G C
But walk right in, woman, sit right down.
G C G C
I will keep on loving you; I play the clown.

Chorus 3

G C G
Bend down low,
C G C G C
Let me tell you what I know now;
G C G
Bend down low,
C G C G C
Let me tell you what I know.

Coda

|: G C | G C | G C | G C :| *Repeat to fade w/vocal ad lib.*

Cry To Me

Words & Music by
Bob Marley

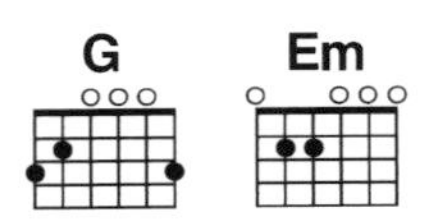

Intro | G | Em | G | Em ||

Chorus 1

```
G        Em                      G       Em
Cry to me, now, you gonna cry to me, yeah.
```

Verse 1

```
                 G                              Em
You're gonna walk back through the heartaches;
                 G                              Em
You're gonna walk back through the pain;
G                                    Em
(Shed those) shed those lonely teardrops,
      G                                   Em
The reaction of your cheating game.
```

Chorus 2

```
                G        Em
You got to cry to me, now.
                    G                 Em
You're gonna cry, cry, cry to me, yeah.
```

Verse 2

```
          G                                Em
Yeah,   Lord knows how I get from the heartaches;
G                Em
   Lord that leadeth me, yeah.
G                     Em
   And now I'm by the still water.
G                             Em
   You've got to cry to me, yeah.
```

Chorus 3

```
                G        Em
You gonna cry to me now;
                   G                  Em
You've got to cry,  cry, cry to me, yeah.
```

Verse 3

```
                G                        Em
You're gonna spend those lonely hours.
                G                     Em
You're gonna shed those lonely tears;
G                                          Em
(Walk back) walk back through the heartaches;
G                                          Em
(Walk back) walk back through the pain;
G                                   Em
(Shed those) shed those lonely teardrops,
     G                              Em
The reaction of your cheating game.
```

Chorus 4

```
                G       Em
You're gonna cry to me, now.
             G               Em
You got to cry, cry, cry to me, yeah.
```

Verse 4

```
           G
Saying (walk back) don't know,
               Em
Know how I get from the heartaches;
G                        Em
(Walk back) Lord that leadeth me, yeah.
 G                    Em
{ (Shed those lonely teardrops)
                      I'm    by   the   still water.
     G                             Em
{ (Reaction of your cheating    game)
                              Gonna cry to me now, hey.
```

Outro

```
G                Em
(Cry,) cry (to me.)
G                Em
(Cry,) cry (to me.)
G                Em
(Cry,) cry (to me.)      To Fade
```

Duppy Conqueror

Words & Music by
Bob Marley

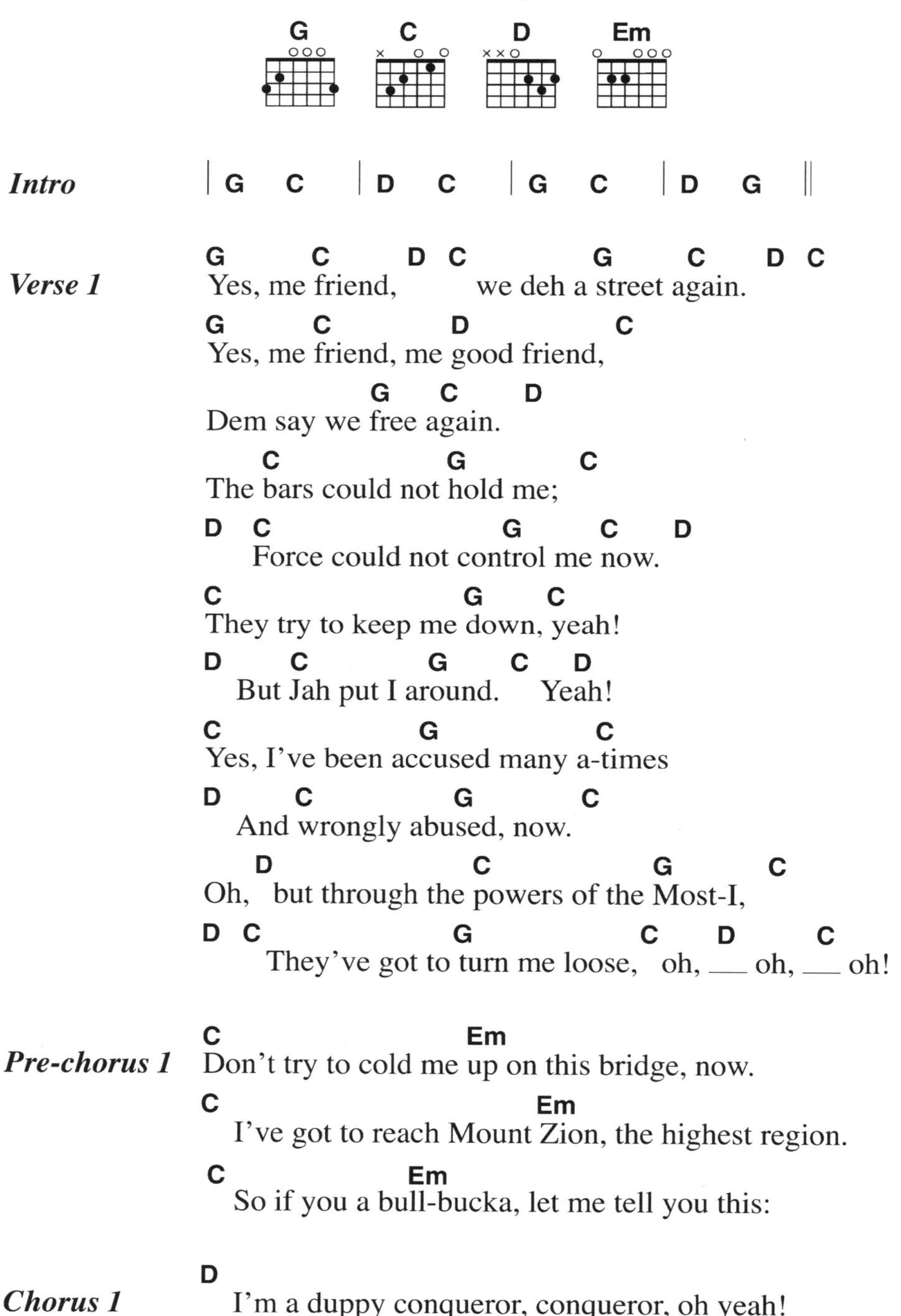

Intro | G C | D C | G C | D G ||

Verse 1

```
G        C        D  C           G        C      D  C
Yes, me friend,       we deh a street again.
G        C              D              C
Yes, me friend, me good friend,
                 G      C       D
Dem say we free again.
      C                G            C
The bars could not hold me;
D   C                       G         C      D
     Force could not control me now.
C                          G       C
They try to keep me down, yeah!
D        C            G        C     D
   But Jah put I around.     Yeah!
C                    G                C
Yes, I've been accused many a-times
D          C              G           C
   And wrongly abused, now.
     D                     C                G          C
Oh,   but through the powers of the Most-I,
D   C                       G                  C        D          C
       They've got to turn me loose,   oh, __ oh, __ oh!
```

Pre-chorus 1

```
C                       Em
Don't try to cold me up on this bridge, now.
C                                  Em
   I've got to reach Mount Zion, the highest region.
C                   Em
   So if you a bull-bucka, let me tell you this:
```

Chorus 1

```
D
   I'm a duppy conqueror, conqueror, oh yeah!
```

```
            G         C         D             C
Verse 2     Yes, me friend, me good friend,
                        G       C   D     C
            We deh a street again,   oh!
            G         C         D             C
            Yes, me friend, me good friend,
                           G    C
            Dem say we free again.

            D       C                              Em
Pre-chorus 2   Oh!   Oh! So don't try to hold me up on this bridge, now.
            C                               Em
               I've got to reach Mount Zion, the highest region.
            C                    Em
               So if you a bull-bucka, let me tell you this:

            D
Chorus 2       I'm a duppy conqueror, conqueror, oh yeah!

            G          C       D C                G      C
Coda        Yes, me friend,          dem say we free again.
            D       C            G          C       D C               G      C
               Oh!   Oh, yeah! Yes, me friend,          dem set we free again.
            D       C G          C          D             C
               Oh!      Yes, me friend, me good friend…
                                                                To Fade
```

The Heathen

Words & Music by
Bob Marley

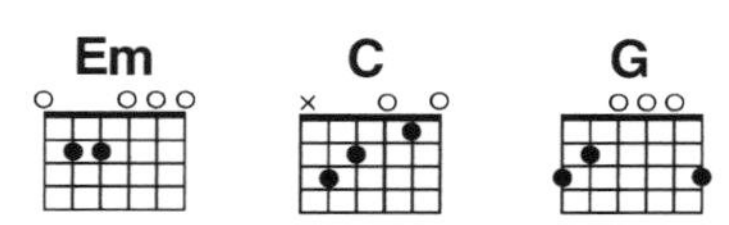

Intro | (Em) (C) (G) | (Em) (C) (G) ||

Chorus 1

```
     Em                  C      G
De heathen back dey 'pon de wall,
         Em                  C       G
Put de heathen back, yeah, 'pon de wall.
     Em                  C      G
De heathen back dey 'pon de wall,
         Em                  C       G
Put de heathen back, yeah, 'pon de wall.
```

Verse 1

```
Em       C          G
   Rise up fallen fighters;
Em                  C          G
   Rise and take your stance again.
Em                       C     Em
   'Tis he who fight and run away,
                C       G
Live to fight another day.
```

Chorus 2 As Chorus 1

Verse 2

```
Em               C        G
   As a man sow, shall he reap,
Em                  C     G
   And I know that talk is cheap.
Em                   C      Em
   But the hotter the bat - tle,
                    C      G
Ah, the sweeter Jah victory.
```

Chorus 3

```
       Em                    C     G
‖: De heathen back dey 'pon de wall,
        Em                      C      G
Put de heathen back, yeah, 'pon de wall.
    Em                   C      G
De heathen back dey 'pon de wall,
        Em                      C      G
Put de heathen back, yeah, 'pon de wall.  :‖
```

Verse 3

```
Em        C          G
   Rise up fallen fighters;
Em                      C         G
   Rise and take your stance again.
Em                        C    Em
   'Tis he who fight and run away,
              C    G
Live to fight another day.
```

Chorus 4

```
       Em                    C     G
‖: De heathen back dey 'pon de wall,
        Em                      C      G
Put de heathen back, yeah, 'pon de wall.
    Em                   C      G
De heathen back dey 'pon de wall,
        Em                      C      G
Put de heathen back, yeah, 'pon de wall.  :‖   Repeat to fade
```

Jah Live

Words & Music by
Bob Marley & Lee Perry

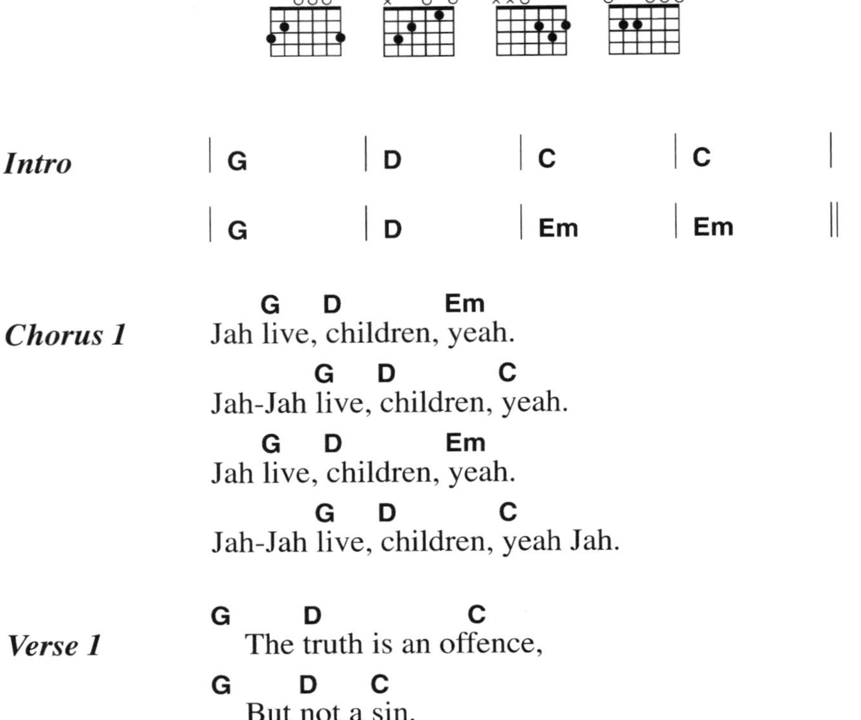

Intro

| G | D | C | C |
| G | D | Em | Em ||

Chorus 1

G D Em
Jah live, children, yeah.
G D C
Jah-Jah live, children, yeah.
G D Em
Jah live, children, yeah.
G D C
Jah-Jah live, children, yeah Jah.

Verse 1

G D C
The truth is an offence,
G D C
But not a sin.
G D C
Is he who laugh last, children,
G D C
Is he who win.
G D C
Is a foolish dog
G D C
Bark at a flying bird.
G D C
One sheep a-must learn, children,
G D C
To respect the shepherd.

Chorus 2 As Chorus 1

```
Guitar solo   | G        | D        | C        | C        |
              | G        | D        | Em       | Em       ||

              G      D          C
Verse 2         Fools  say in their heart,
              G               D    C
                "Rasta, your god is dead."
              G      D   C           G
                But I'n'I know Jah-Jah Dread,
                   D       C
              It shall be Dreader Dread.

                 G   D        Em
Chorus 3      Jah live, children, yeah.
                    G   D       C
              Jah-Jah live, children, yeah.
                 G   D        Em
              Jah live, children, yeah.
                    G   D       C
              Jah-Jah live, children, yeah Jah.

              G     D    C
Verse 3         Let Jah  arise
              G             D              C
                Now that the enemies are scattered.
              G     D    C
                Let Jah  arise,
                 G            D              C
              The enemies, the enemies are scattered.

                 G   D        Em
Coda          Jah live, children, yeah.
                    G   D       C
              Jah-Jah live, children, yeah...            To Fade
```

Mellow Mood

Words & Music by
Bob Marley

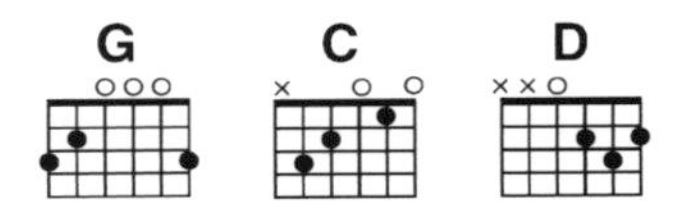

Intro | G C | G D | G C | G C D ||

Verse 1

```
G    C                    G    D
  I'll play your favourite song, darling.
G          C               G   D
  We can rock it all night long, darling.
G          C      G    D
  'Cause I've got love, darling;
G   C           G    C    D    G
   Love, sweet love, dar - ling.
```

Verse 2

```
C                        G       C  D
  While the mood has got me,
G    C              G        C  D
  So  let the music rock me.
G          C      G    D
  'Cause I've got love, darling;
G   C           G    C    D    G
   Love, sweet love, dar - ling.
```

Verse 3

```
C              G      C  D
  Quiet is the night,
G       C              G     C  D
  Please  turn off your light.
G    C                    G    C   D
  I'll play your favourite song, dar - ling.
G          C               G    C    D    G
  We can rock it all night long, dar - ling.
G          C      G    D
  'Cause I've got love, darling;
G   C           G    C    D    G
   Love, sweet love, dar - ling.
```

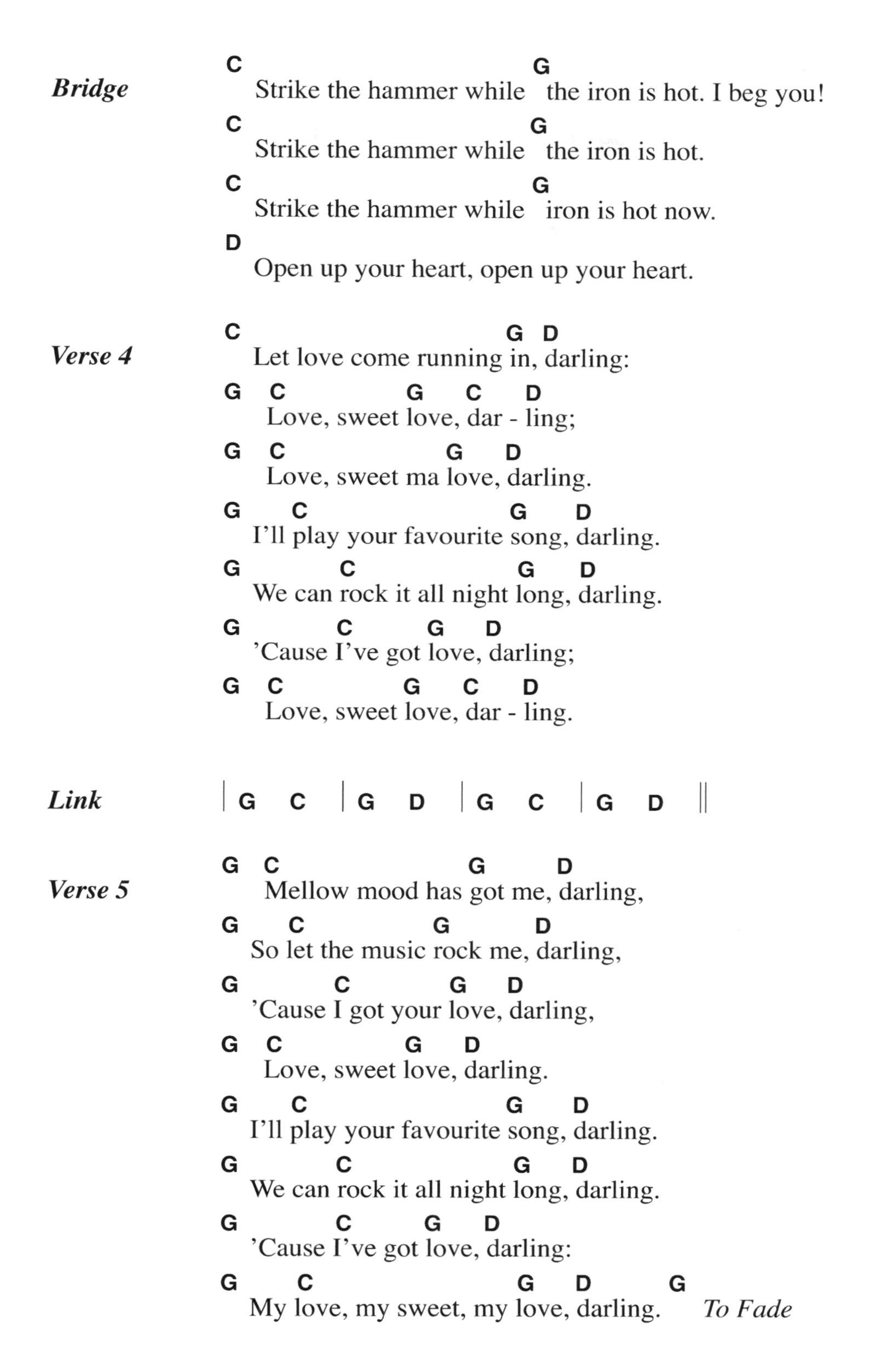

Bridge

C G
Strike the hammer while the iron is hot. I beg you!

C G
Strike the hammer while the iron is hot.

C G
Strike the hammer while iron is hot now.

D
Open up your heart, open up your heart.

Verse 4

C G D
Let love come running in, darling:

G C G C D
Love, sweet love, dar - ling;

G C G D
Love, sweet ma love, darling.

G C G D
I'll play your favourite song, darling.

G C G D
We can rock it all night long, darling.

G C G D
'Cause I've got love, darling;

G C G C D
Love, sweet love, dar - ling.

Link

| G C | G D | G C | G D ||

Verse 5

G C G D
Mellow mood has got me, darling,

G C G D
So let the music rock me, darling,

G C G D
'Cause I got your love, darling,

G C G D
Love, sweet love, darling.

G C G D
I'll play your favourite song, darling.

G C G D
We can rock it all night long, darling.

G C G D
'Cause I've got love, darling:

G C G D G
My love, my sweet, my love, darling. *To Fade*

One Love/People Get Ready

Words & Music by
Bob Marley & Curtis Mayfield

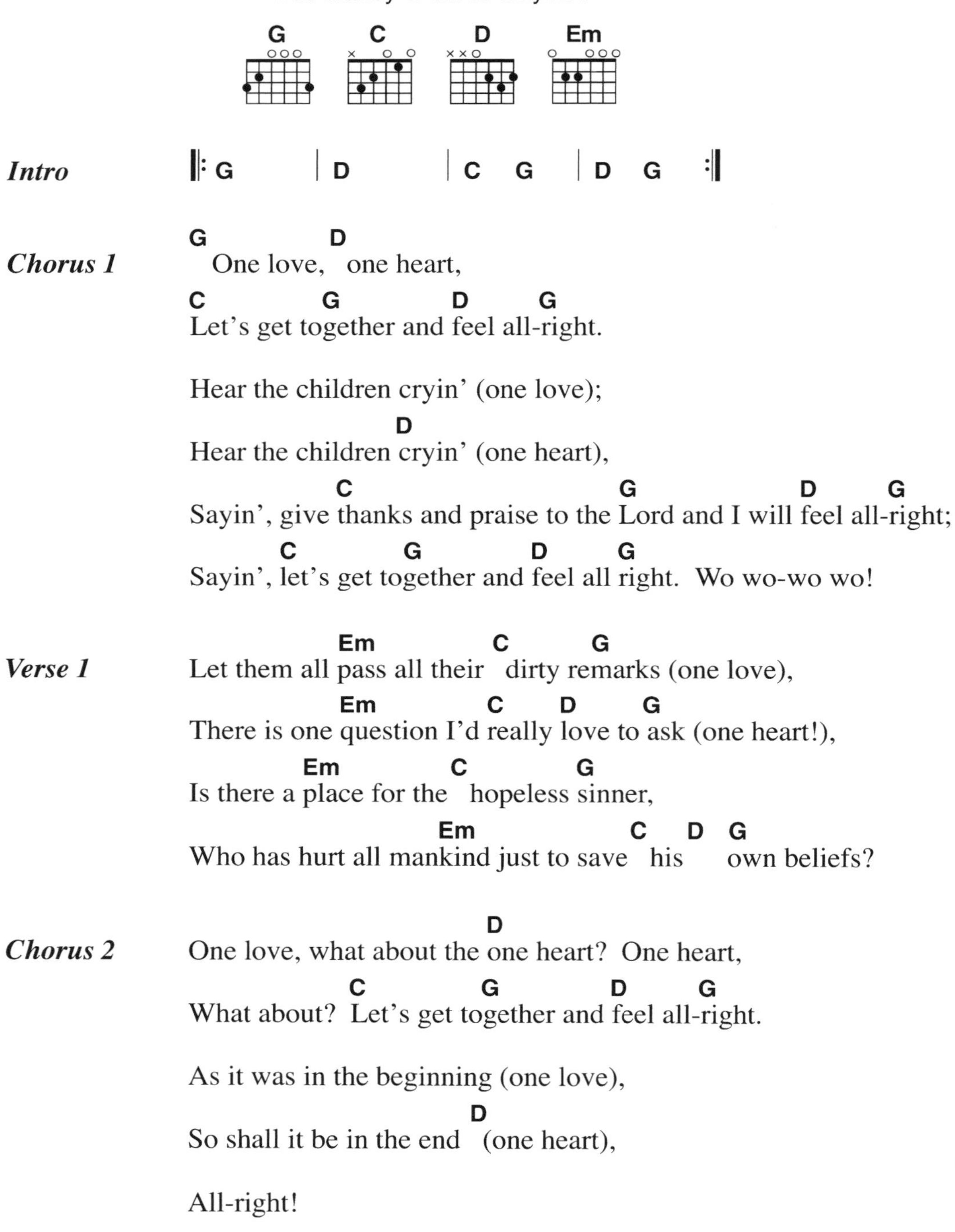

```
               C                              G                D       G
cont.          Give thanks and praise to the Lord and I will feel all-right,
               C          G          D      G
               Let's get together and feel all-right.

               One more thing!

                          Em        C                     G
Verse 2        Let's get together to fight this Holy Armageddon (one love),
                            Em                        C   D     G
               So when the Man comes there will   be no, no doom (one song).
                            Em          C                G
               Have pity on those whose chances grows t'inner;
                              Em                       C     D     G
               There ain't no hiding place from the Father of Creation.

                                                         D
Chorus 3        Sayin' one love, what about the one heart?  (one heart),

               What about the…
               C          G          D      G
               Let's get together and feel all right.

               I'm pleadin' to mankind! (one love),
                     D
               Oh, Lord! (One heart.) Wo-ooh!
                    C                              G                D       G
               Give thanks and praise to the Lord and I will feel all-right,
               C          G          D      G
               Let's get together and feel all-right.
                    C                              G                D       G
               Give thanks and praise to the Lord and I will feel all-right,
               C          G          D      G
               Let's get together and feel all-right.     To Fade
```

No Woman, No Cry

Words & Music by
Vincent Ford

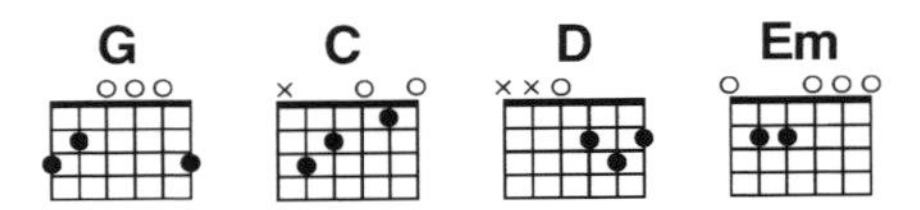

Intro ‖: G D | Em C | G C | G D :‖

Chorus 1

G D Em C
No woman, no cry,
G C G D
No woman, no cry,
G D Em C
No woman, no cry,
G C G D
No woman, no cry.

Verse 1

G D Em C
Say, say, said I remember when we used to sit
G D Em C
In the government yard in Trenchtown,
G D Em C
Oba-observing the hypocrites
G D Em C
As they would mingle with the good people we meet.
G D Em C
Good friends we have had, oh good friends we've lost
G D Em C
Along the way.
G D Em C
In this bright future you can't forget your past,
G D Em C
So dry your tears, I say, and

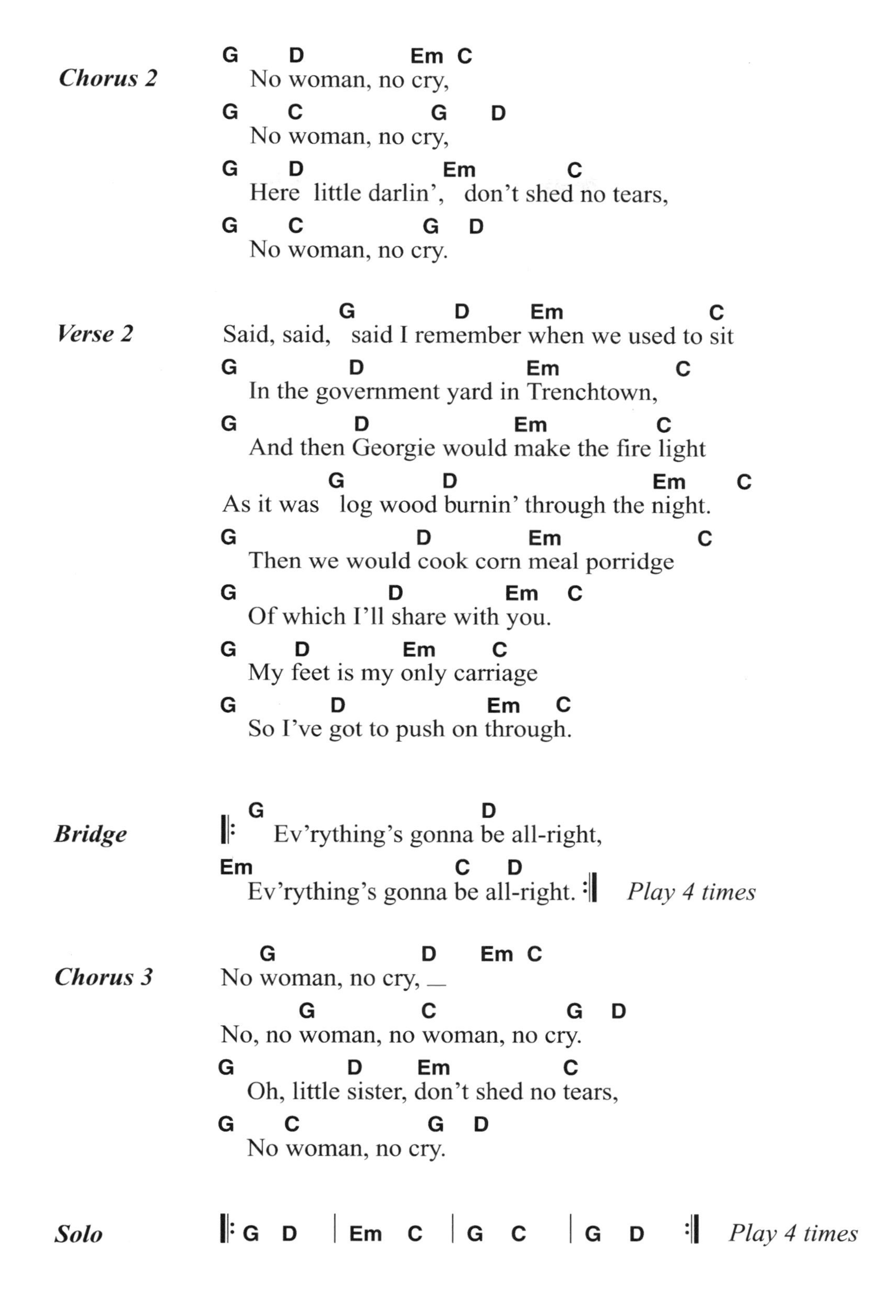
Chorus 2
G D Em C
No woman, no cry,
G C G D
No woman, no cry,
G D Em C
Here little darlin', don't shed no tears,
G C G D
No woman, no cry.
Verse 2
G D Em C
Said, said, said I remember when we used to sit
G D Em C
In the government yard in Trenchtown,
G D Em C
And then Georgie would make the fire light
G D Em C
As it was log wood burnin' through the night.
G D Em C
Then we would cook corn meal porridge
G D Em C
Of which I'll share with you.
G D Em C
My feet is my only carriage
G D Em C
So I've got to push on through.
Bridge
G D
Ev'rything's gonna be all-right,
Em C D
Ev'rything's gonna be all-right.
Play 4 times
Chorus 3
G D Em C
No woman, no cry,
G C G D
No, no woman, no woman, no cry.
G D Em C
Oh, little sister, don't shed no tears,
G C G D
No woman, no cry.
Solo
G D | Em C | G C | G D
Play 4 times

Verse 3

G D Em C
Said, said, said I remember when we used to sit
G D Em C
In the government yard in Trenchtown,
G D Em C
And then Georgie would make the fire light
G D Em C
As it was log wood burnin' through the night.
G D Em C
Then we would cook corn meal porridge
G D Em C
Of which I'll share with you.
G D Em C
My feet is my only carriage
G D Em
So I've got to push on through,
C D
But while I'm gone I mean.

Chorus 4

G D Em C
No woman, no cry,
G C G D
No woman, no cry,
G D Em C
Oh c'mon little darlin', say don't shed no tears,
G C G D
No woman, no cry, yeah!

Chorus 5

G D Em C
(Little darlin', don't shed no tears,
G C G D
No woman, no cry.
G C G G
Little sister, don't shed no tears,
C G D
No woman, no cry.)

Coda

| G D | Em C | G C | G D |
| G D | Em C | G C | G ‖

Ride Natty Ride

Words & Music by
Bob Marley

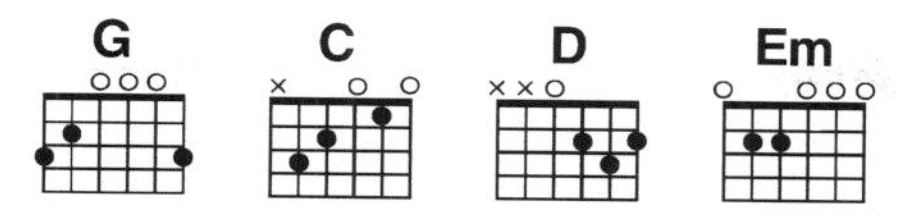

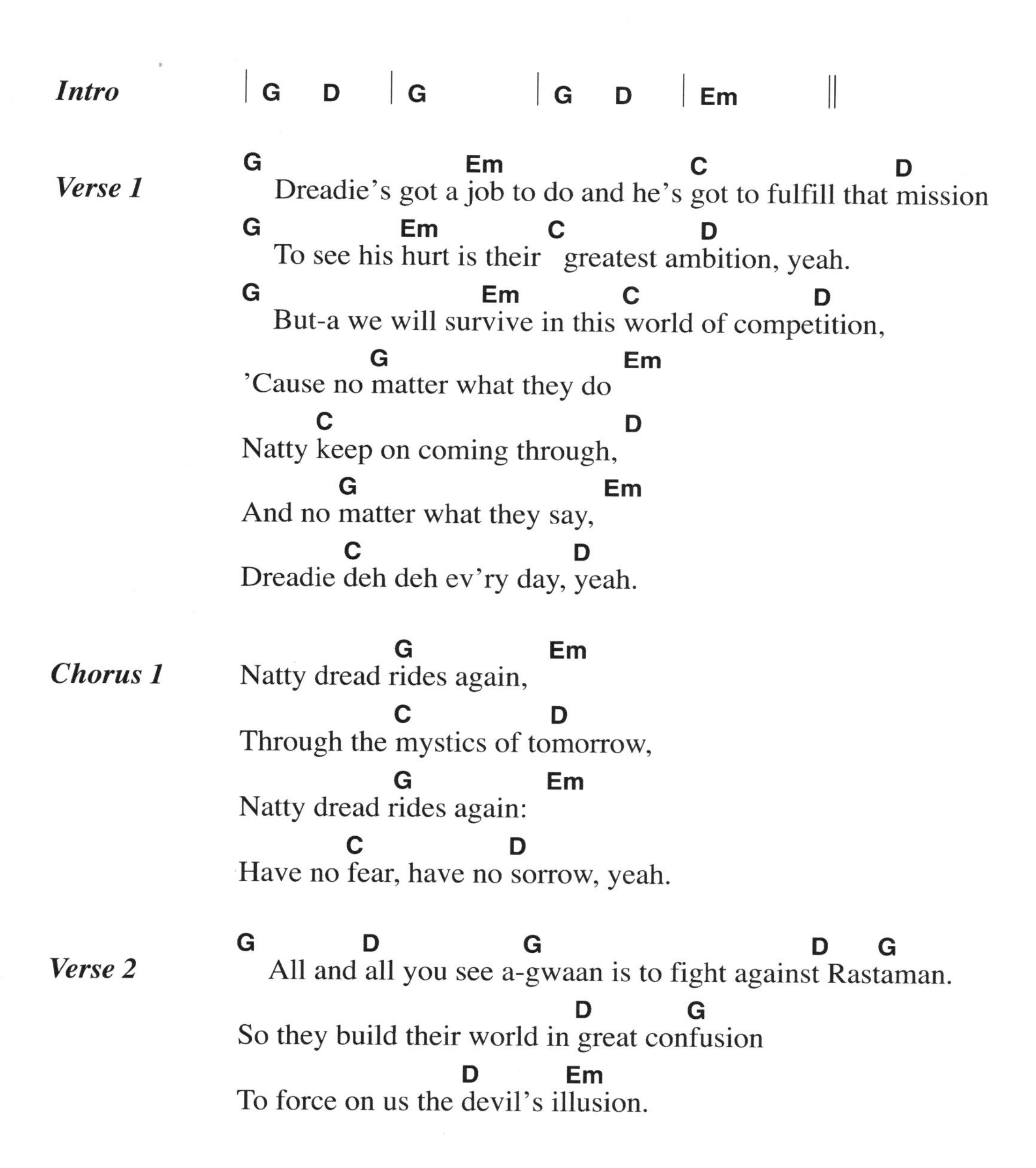

Intro

| G D | G | G D | Em ||

Verse 1

G Em C D
Dreadie's got a job to do and he's got to fulfill that mission
G Em C D
To see his hurt is their greatest ambition, yeah.
G Em C D
But-a we will survive in this world of competition,
G Em
'Cause no matter what they do
C D
Natty keep on coming through,
G Em
And no matter what they say,
C D
Dreadie deh deh ev'ry day, yeah.

Chorus 1

G Em
Natty dread rides again,
C D
Through the mystics of tomorrow,
G Em
Natty dread rides again:
C D
Have no fear, have no sorrow, yeah.

Verse 2

G D G D G
All and all you see a-gwaan is to fight against Rastaman.
D G
So they build their world in great confusion
D Em
To force on us the devil's illusion.

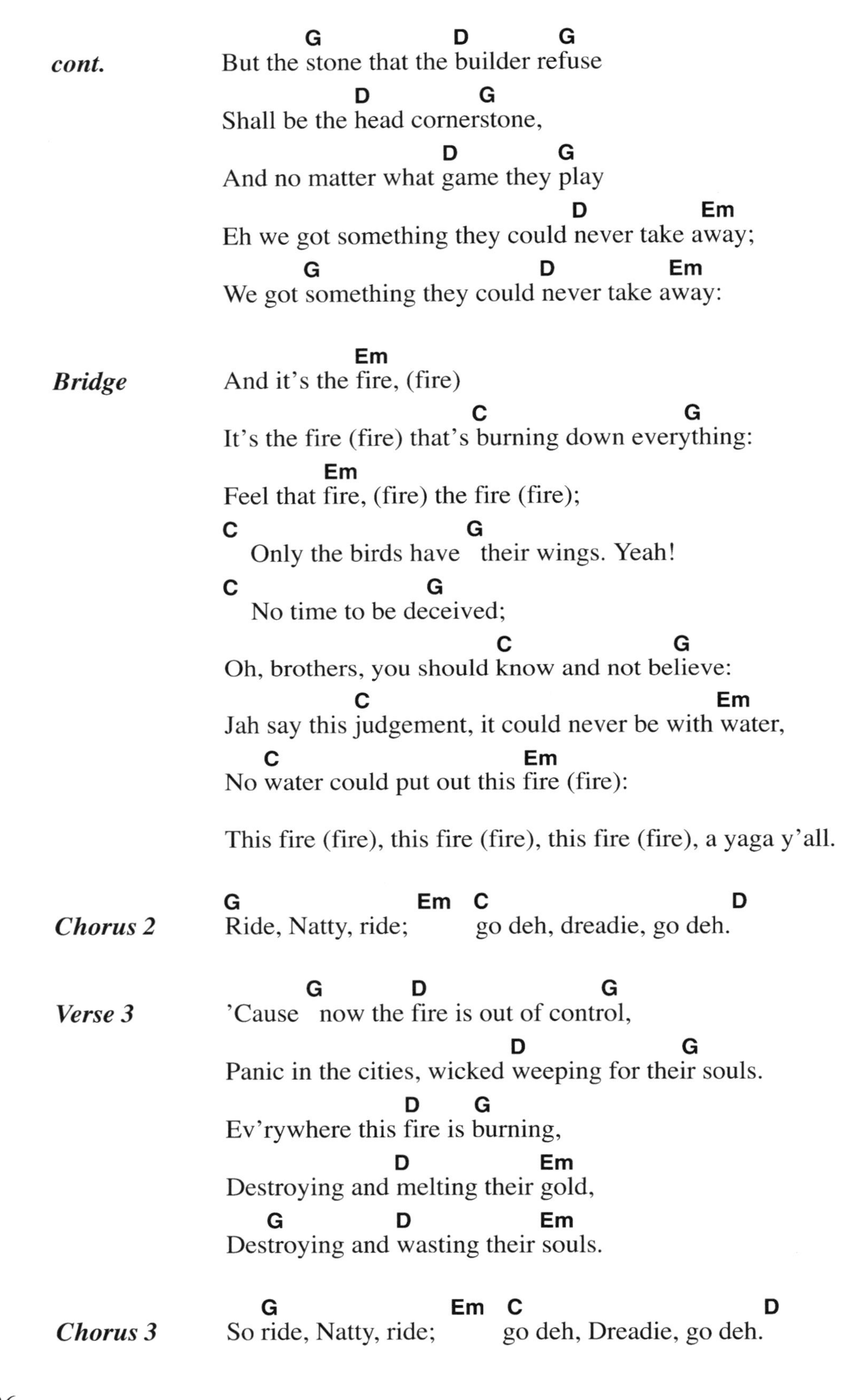

cont.

G D G
But the stone that the builder refuse
D G
Shall be the head cornerstone,
D G
And no matter what game they play
D Em
Eh we got something they could never take away;
G D Em
We got something they could never take away:

Bridge

Em
And it's the fire, (fire)
C G
It's the fire (fire) that's burning down everything:
Em
Feel that fire, (fire) the fire (fire);
C G
Only the birds have their wings. Yeah!
C G
No time to be deceived;
C G
Oh, brothers, you should know and not believe:
C Em
Jah say this judgement, it could never be with water,
C Em
No water could put out this fire (fire):

This fire (fire), this fire (fire), this fire (fire), a yaga y'all.

Chorus 2

G Em C D
Ride, Natty, ride; go deh, dreadie, go deh.

Verse 3

G D G
'Cause now the fire is out of control,
D G
Panic in the cities, wicked weeping for their souls.
D G
Ev'rywhere this fire is burning,
D Em
Destroying and melting their gold,
G D Em
Destroying and wasting their souls.

Chorus 3

G Em C D
So ride, Natty, ride; go deh, Dreadie, go deh.

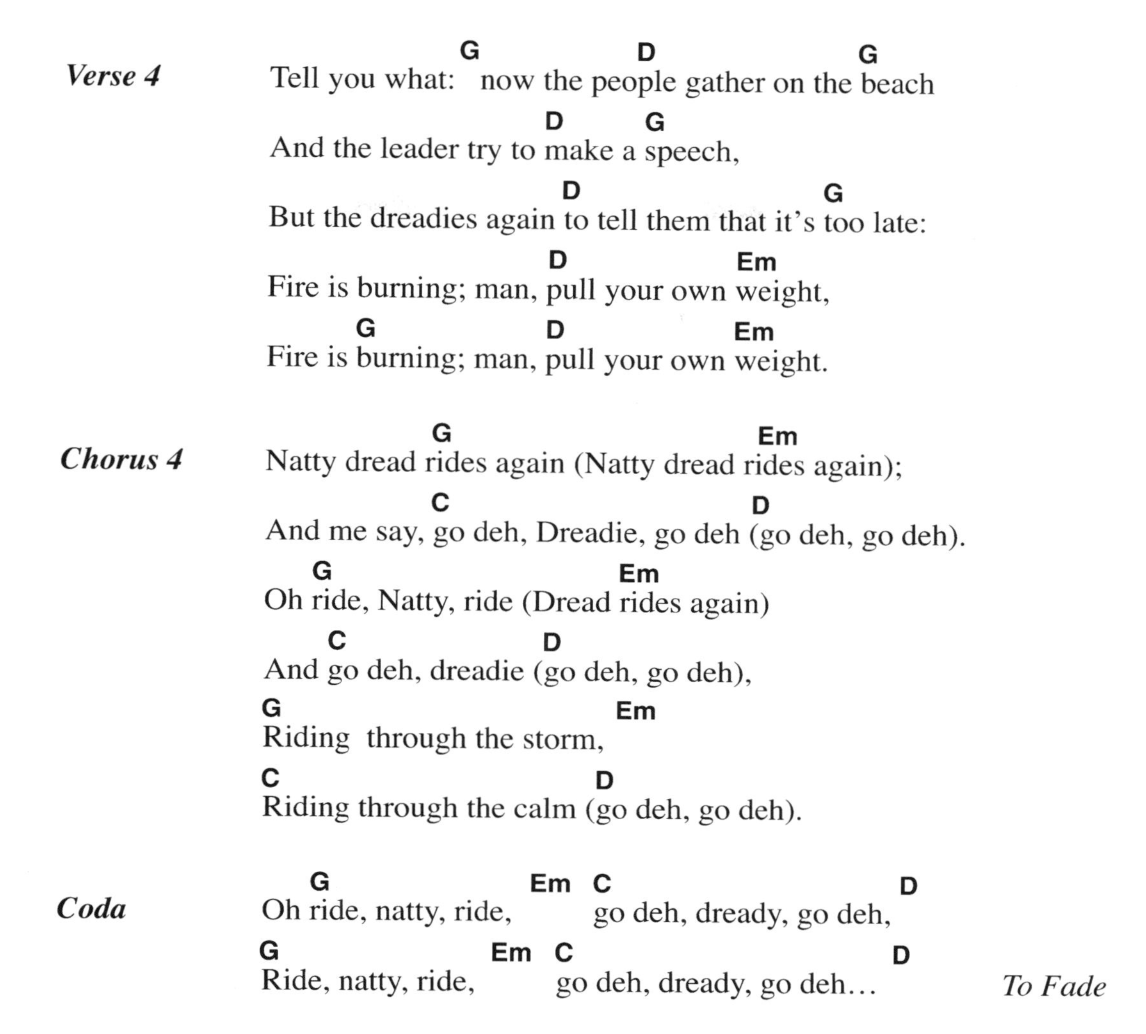

Verse 4

G D G
Tell you what: now the people gather on the beach

D G
And the leader try to make a speech,

D G
But the dreadies again to tell them that it's too late:

D Em
Fire is burning; man, pull your own weight,

G D Em
Fire is burning; man, pull your own weight.

Chorus 4

G Em
Natty dread rides again (Natty dread rides again);

C D
And me say, go deh, Dreadie, go deh (go deh, go deh).

G Em
Oh ride, Natty, ride (Dread rides again)

C D
And go deh, dreadie (go deh, go deh),

G Em
Riding through the storm,

C D
Riding through the calm (go deh, go deh).

Coda

G Em C D
Oh ride, natty, ride, go deh, dready, go deh,

G Em C D
Ride, natty, ride, go deh, dready, go deh… *To Fade*

Rastaman Live Up!

Words & Music by
Bob Marley & Lee Perry

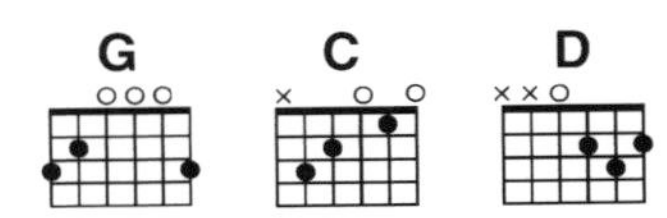

Chorus 1

N.G. G
Rastaman, live up.
C D
Bongoman, don't give up.
G
Congoman, live up, yeah.
C D
Bingiman don't give up.

Verse 1

G G C D
Keep your culture, don't be afraid of the vulture.
G G C D
Grow your dreadlocks, don't be afraid of the wolfpack.

Chorus 2

N.G. G
Rastaman, live up.
C D
Bingiman don't give up.
G
Congoman, live up, yeah.
C D
Bongoman, don't give up.

Verse 2

G G C D
David slew Goliath with a sling and a stone;
G G C D
Samson slew the Philistines with a donkey jawbone.

Chorus 3

G
Iyahman, live up.
C D
Rastaman, don't give up.

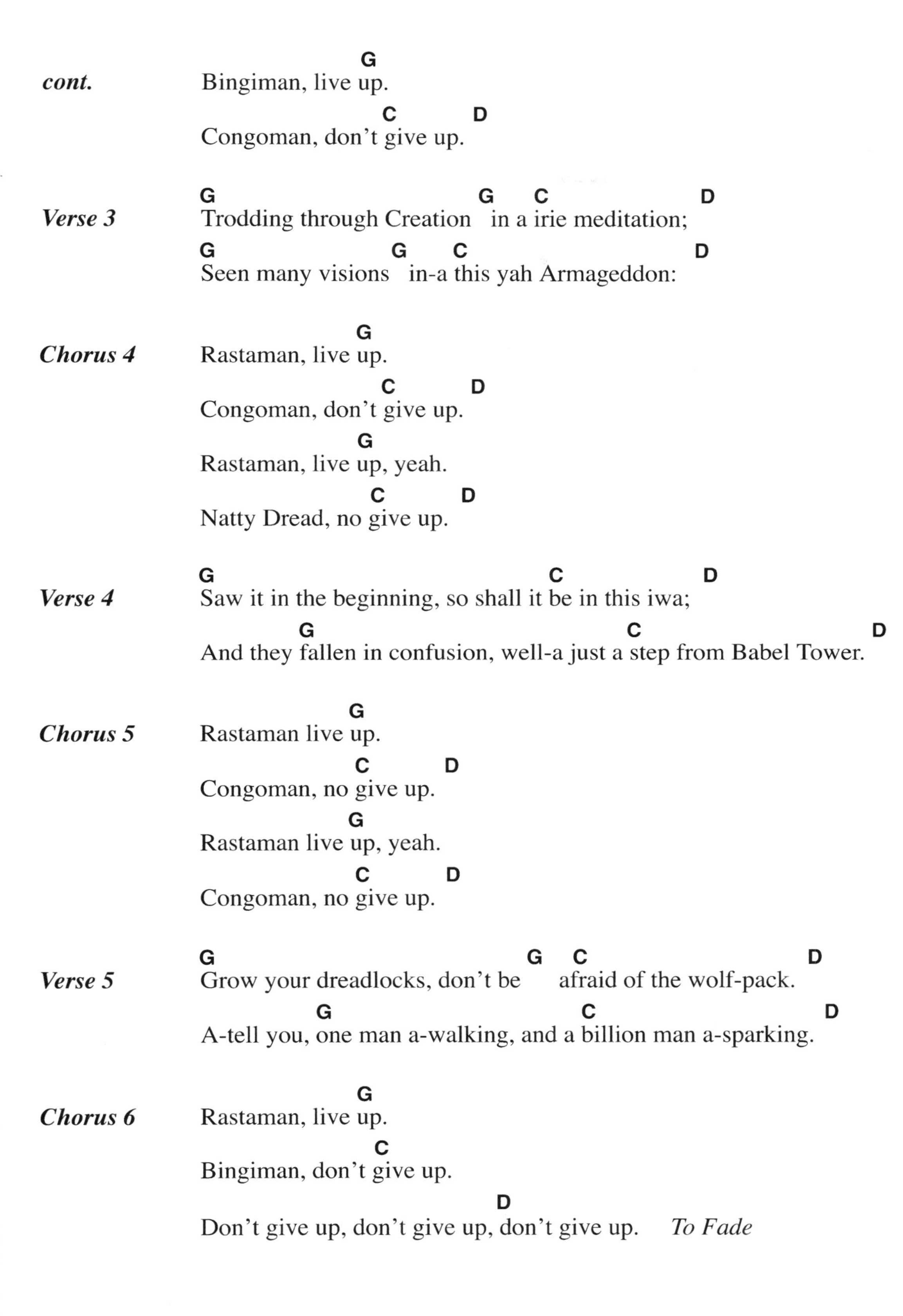

cont.

G
Bingiman, live up.
C D
Congoman, don't give up.

Verse 3

G G C D
Trodding through Creation in a irie meditation;
G G C D
Seen many visions in-a this yah Armageddon:

Chorus 4

G
Rastaman, live up.
C D
Congoman, don't give up.
G
Rastaman, live up, yeah.
C D
Natty Dread, no give up.

Verse 4

G C D
Saw it in the beginning, so shall it be in this iwa;
G C D
And they fallen in confusion, well-a just a step from Babel Tower.

Chorus 5

G
Rastaman live up.
C D
Congoman, no give up.
G
Rastaman live up, yeah.
C D
Congoman, no give up.

Verse 5

G G C D
Grow your dreadlocks, don't be afraid of the wolf-pack.
G C D
A-tell you, one man a-walking, and a billion man a-sparking.

Chorus 6

G
Rastaman, live up.
C
Bingiman, don't give up.
D
Don't give up, don't give up, don't give up. *To Fade*

Redemption Song

Words & Music by
Bob Marley

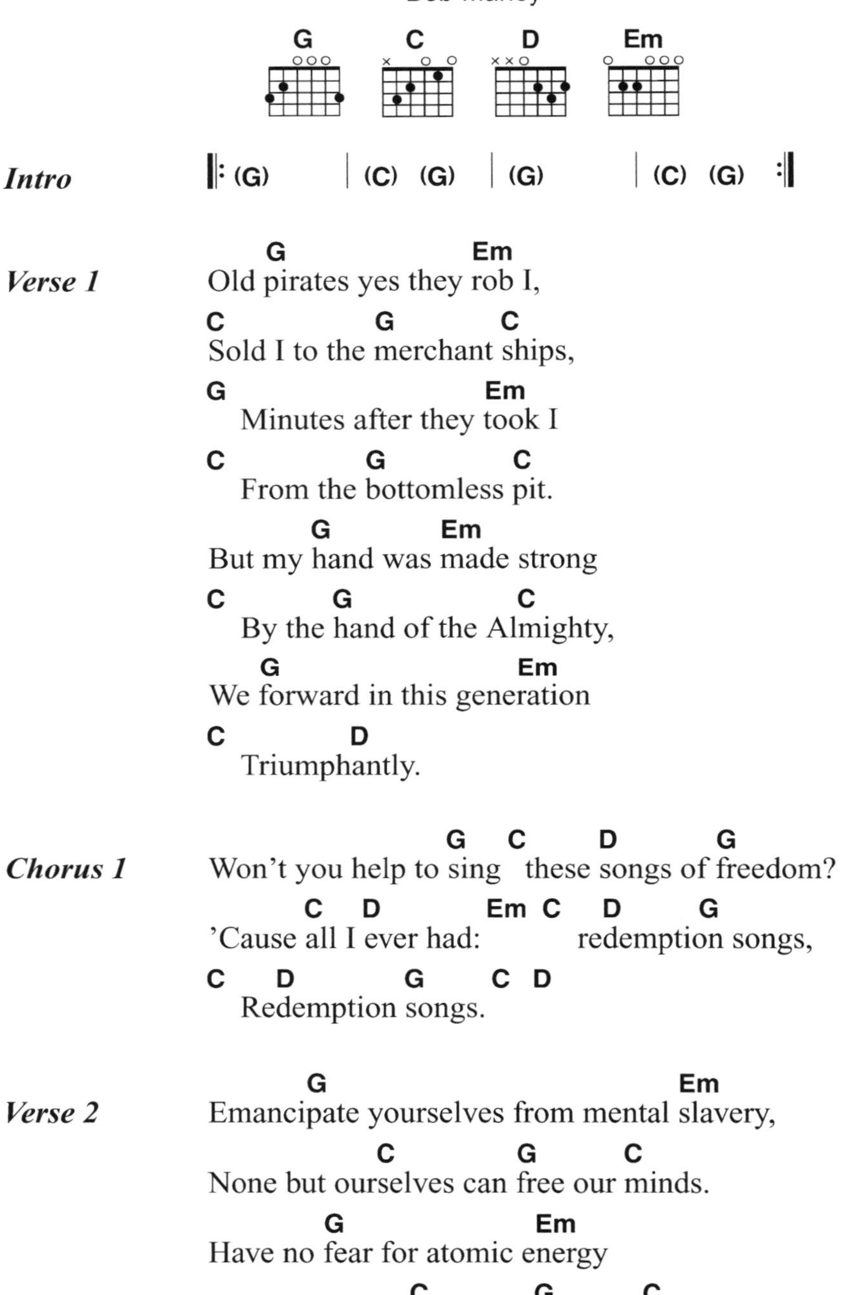

Intro | |: (G) | (C) (G) | (G) | (C) (G) :| |

Verse 1

```
    G                  Em
Old pirates yes they rob I,
C           G          C
Sold I to the merchant ships,
G                        Em
   Minutes after they took I
C              G           C
   From the bottomless pit.
        G          Em
But my hand was made strong
C          G                C
   By the hand of the Almighty,
     G                       Em
We forward in this generation
C              D
   Triumphantly.
```

Chorus 1

```
                        G    C       D          G
Won't you help to sing   these songs of freedom?
          C   D           Em  C     D        G
'Cause all I ever had:          redemption songs,
C     D          G      C  D
   Redemption songs.
```

Verse 2

```
          G                               Em
Emancipate yourselves from mental slavery,
                 C             G         C
None but ourselves can free our minds.
           G                 Em
Have no fear for atomic energy
                     C          G         C
'Cause none of them can stop the time.
```

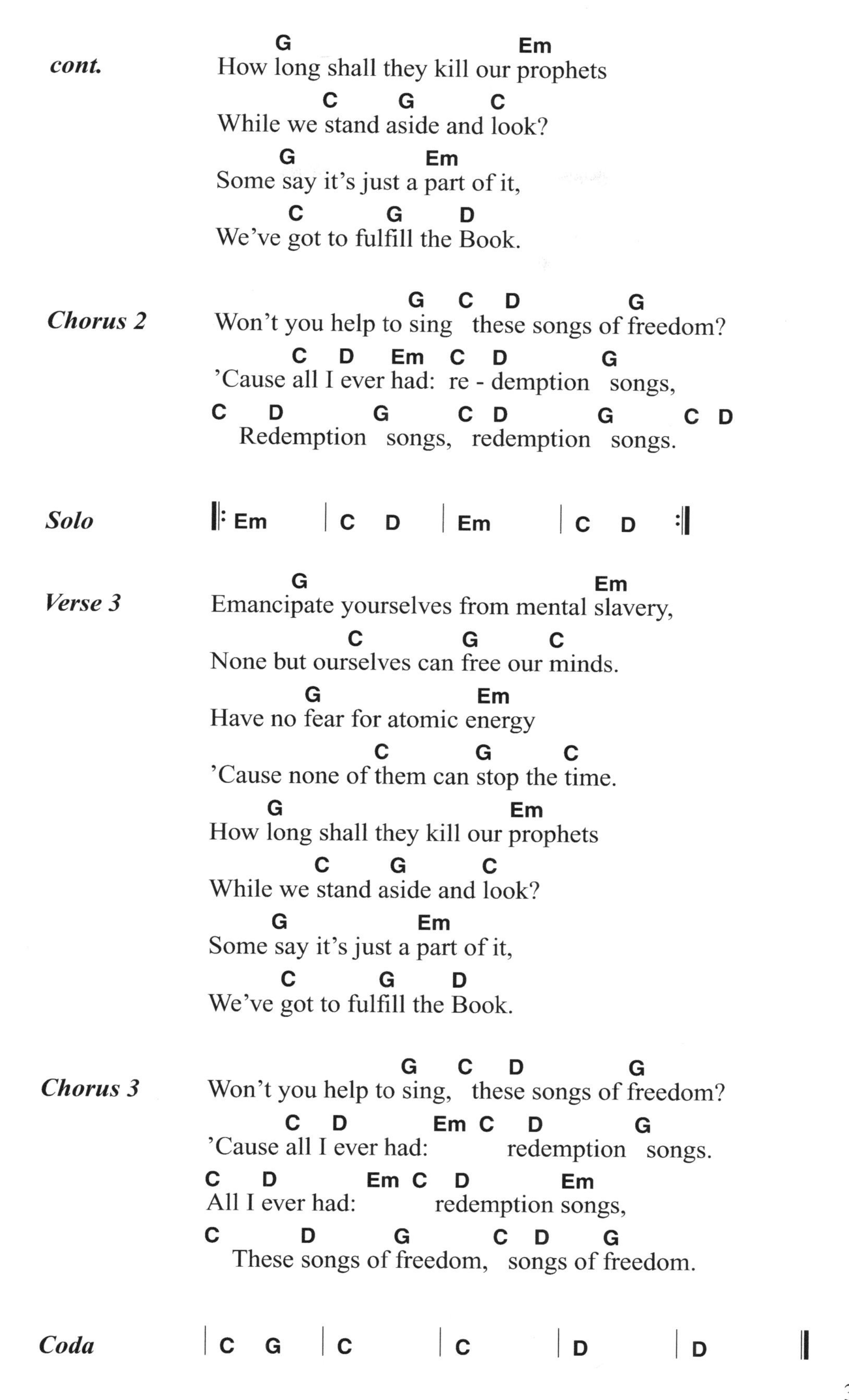

cont.

G Em
How long shall they kill our prophets
C G C
While we stand aside and look?
G Em
Some say it's just a part of it,
C G D
We've got to fulfill the Book.

Chorus 2

G C D G
Won't you help to sing these songs of freedom?
C D Em C D G
'Cause all I ever had: re - demption songs,
C D G C D G C D
Redemption songs, redemption songs.

Solo

|: Em | C D | Em | C D :|

Verse 3

G Em
Emancipate yourselves from mental slavery,
C G C
None but ourselves can free our minds.
G Em
Have no fear for atomic energy
C G C
'Cause none of them can stop the time.
G Em
How long shall they kill our prophets
C G C
While we stand aside and look?
G Em
Some say it's just a part of it,
C G D
We've got to fulfill the Book.

Chorus 3

G C D G
Won't you help to sing, these songs of freedom?
C D Em C D G
'Cause all I ever had: redemption songs.
C D Em C D Em
All I ever had: redemption songs,
C D G C D G
These songs of freedom, songs of freedom.

Coda

| C G | C | C | D | D ||

Smile Jamaica

Words & Music by
Bob Marley

G C D Em

Intro | Em | Em | Em | Em ||

Verse 1
```
C                D
  Feeling out,   feeling down:
C                           D
  This feeling wouldn't leave me alone.
C                              D
  Then up came-a one that said:
C               D                        Em
  "Hey, dread, fly, natty dread, and smile!"
```

Chorus 1
```
      Em
(In Jamaica) want you to smile (in Jamaica, y'all).

Get it together right now  (in Jamaica).

Get things together right now (in Jamaica, y'all).
```

Verse 2
```
C                    D
  (Soulful town, roots people),
C                         D
  Said, I see you're having fun,
C                                  D
  Rocking to the roots man rocker,
C                 D
  Oh island in the sun.
```

Chorus 2
```
Em
  (In Jamaica) want you to get (in Jamaica, y'all)

Get this together right now (in Jamaica),

Get it together, right now (in Jamaica, y'all).
```

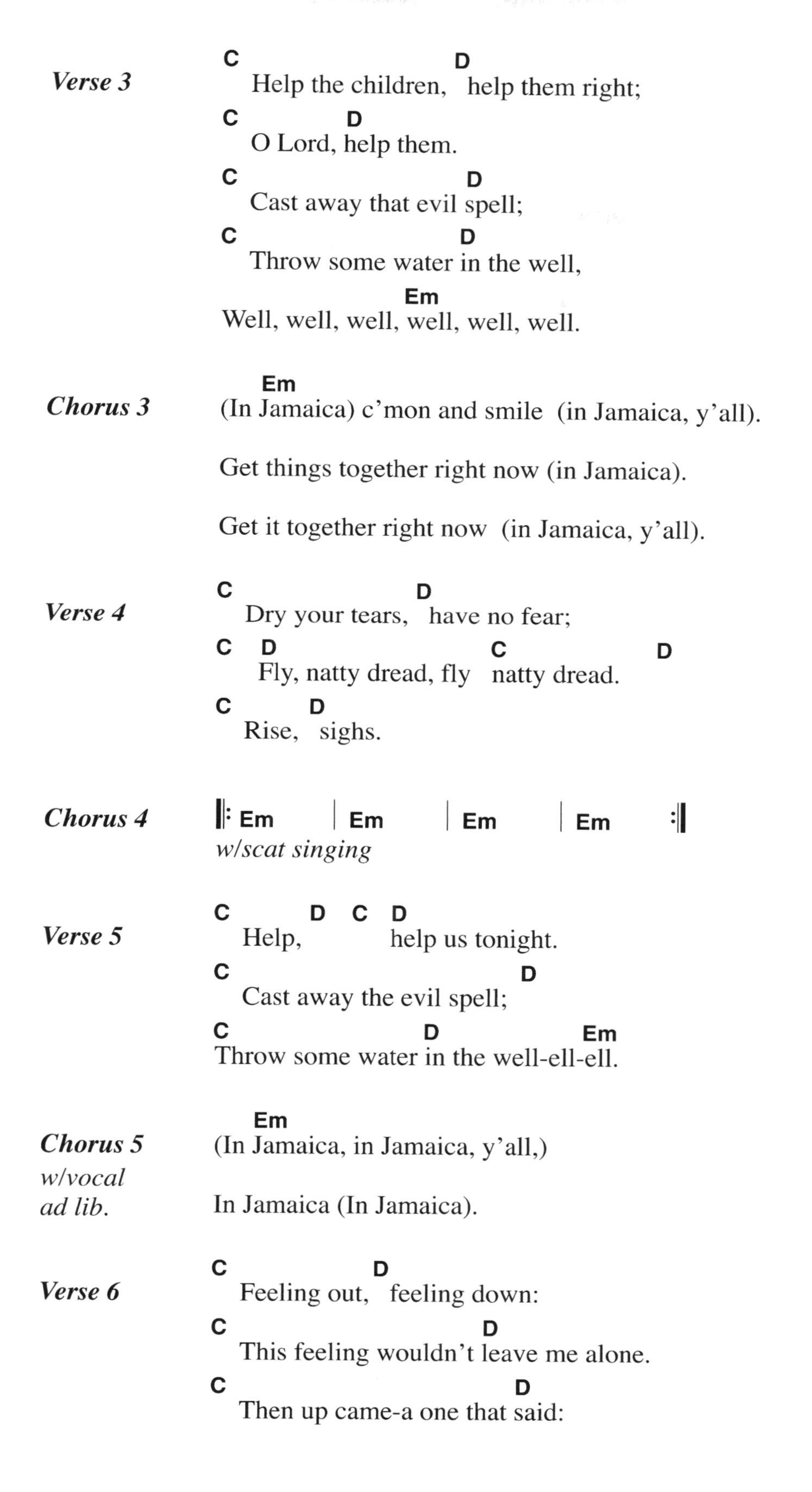

Verse 3

C D
Help the children, help them right;
C D
O Lord, help them.
C D
Cast away that evil spell;
C D
Throw some water in the well,
Em
Well, well, well, well, well, well.

Chorus 3

Em
(In Jamaica) c'mon and smile (in Jamaica, y'all).

Get things together right now (in Jamaica).

Get it together right now (in Jamaica, y'all).

Verse 4

C D
Dry your tears, have no fear;
C D C D
Fly, natty dread, fly natty dread.
C D
Rise, sighs.

Chorus 4

𝄆 Em | Em | Em | Em 𝄇
w/scat singing

Verse 5

C D C D
Help, help us tonight.
C D
Cast away the evil spell;
C D Em
Throw some water in the well-ell-ell.

Chorus 5
w/vocal ad lib.

Em
(In Jamaica, in Jamaica, y'all,)

In Jamaica (In Jamaica).

Verse 6

C D
Feeling out, feeling down:
C D
This feeling wouldn't leave me alone.
C D
Then up came-a one that said:

cont.

C D Em
"Hey, dread, fly, natty dread, and smile!"

In Jamaica, in Jamaica y'all.

Instrumental

| Em | Em | Em | Em | C | D |

| C | D | C | C D | C | D |

| Em | Em | Em | Em |
In Ja - maica, In Ja - maica, y'all.

| Em | Em | Em | Em | C | D |

| C | D | C | C D | C | D |

||: Em | Em | Em | Em :||

Verse 7

C D
Dry your tears, have no fear;
C D | C | C D |
Fly, natty dread.
C D
Rise, sighs.

Chorus 6

||: Em | Em | Em | Em :||
w/scat singing

Verse 8

C D C D
Help, help, help us tonight.
C D C D
Evil spell; In the well.

Chorus 7

Em
||: (In Jamaica, in Jamaica, y'all.) :||
w/vocal ad lib.

Instrumental | (C) | (D) | (C) | (D) | (C) | (C) (D) | (C) | (D)

Chorus 8

Em
||: (In Jamaica, in Jamaica, y'all.) :||
w/vocal ad lib.

| C | D | C ||

Survival

Words & Music by
Bob Marley

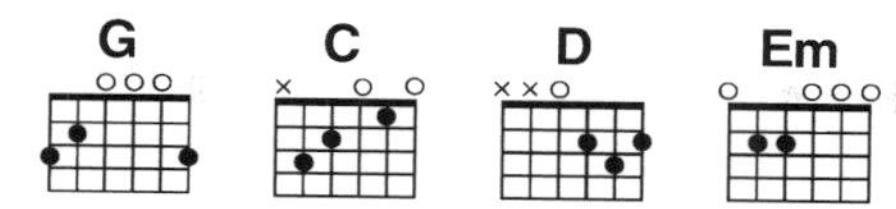


```
             Em
Intro          (Ow, ow-ow-ow, ow, ow-ow-ow-ow.) Yeah, yeah, yeah.

             Em                               C               Em
Verse 1      How can you be sitting there telling me that you care,

             That you care,
                                                           C
             When every time I look around, the people suffer in the suffering
                     Em
             In every way, in everywhere?
                  C           Em         D
             Say: na-na-na-na-na (na na-na na).

             N.C.           Em
Chorus 1     We're the survivors, yes, the black survivors.

                               Em
Verse 2      I tell you what: some people got everything,

             Some people got nothing.

             Some people got hopes and dreams,

             Some people got ways and means.
             C            Em         D
             Na-na-na-na-na (na na-na na).

             N.C.           Em
Chorus 2     We're the survivors, yes, the black survivors,

             Yes, we're the survivors, like Daniel out of the lions' den.

             Survivors, survivors.
```

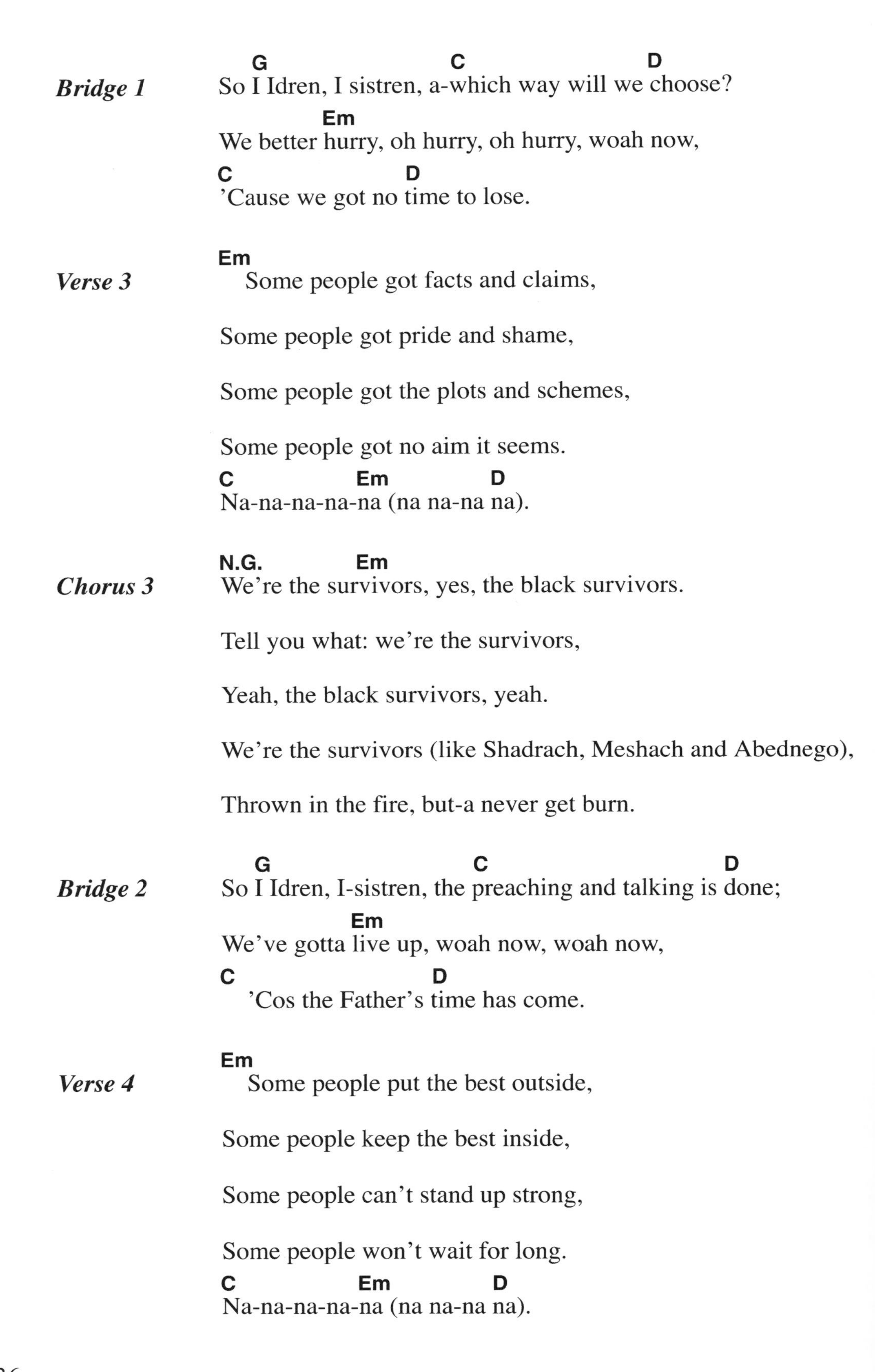

Bridge 1

G **C** **D**
So I Idren, I sistren, a-which way will we choose?
Em
We better hurry, oh hurry, oh hurry, woah now,
C **D**
'Cause we got no time to lose.

Verse 3

Em
Some people got facts and claims,

Some people got pride and shame,

Some people got the plots and schemes,

Some people got no aim it seems.
C **Em** **D**
Na-na-na-na-na (na na-na na).

Chorus 3

N.G. **Em**
We're the survivors, yes, the black survivors.

Tell you what: we're the survivors,

Yeah, the black survivors, yeah.

We're the survivors (like Shadrach, Meshach and Abednego),

Thrown in the fire, but-a never get burn.

Bridge 2

G **C** **D**
So I Idren, I-sistren, the preaching and talking is done;
Em
We've gotta live up, woah now, woah now,
C **D**
'Cos the Father's time has come.

Verse 4

Em
Some people put the best outside,

Some people keep the best inside,

Some people can't stand up strong,

Some people won't wait for long.
C **Em** **D**
Na-na-na-na-na (na na-na na).

Chorus 4

N.C. Em
We're the survivors in this age of technological inhumanity,

Scientific atrocity (survivors),

Atomic mis-philosophy (black survival),

Nuclear mis-energy.

It's a world that forces lifelong insecurity (black survival).

C Em D
Together now: na-na-na-na-na (na na-na na).

Chorus 5

N.C. Em
We're the survivors, yeah,

We're the survivors,

Yes, the black survivors,

We're the survivors.

A good man is never honoured (survivors)

In his own country (black survival),

Nothing change, nothing strange, (survivors),

Nothing change, nothing strange (black survivors). *To Fade*

Soul Shakedown Party

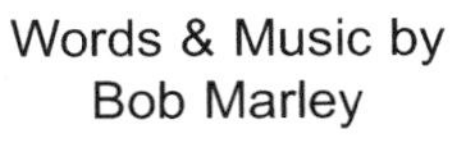

Words & Music by
Bob Marley

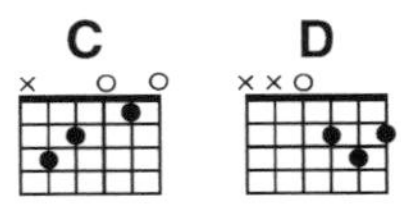

Intro ‖: D | C | D | C :‖

Chorus 1

```
                    D                  C         D      C
We gonna have a soul shakedown   party tonight.
                    D                  C         D      C
We gonna have a soul shakedown   party tonight.
```

Verse 1

```
               D              C              D       C
The way you love-a me,   huh, it's all-right.
                        D                C
When you put your loving arms around me,
                     D     C
And you hold me   tight,   hold me tight.
          D        C                     D              C
This is my invitation: I got the special vacation;
  D                   C                  D                C
I need your concentration just to feel your vibration.
```

Chorus 2

```
          D                C         D        C
At that soul shakedown   party tonight,
                    D                  C          D       C
We gonna have a soul shakedown   party tonight.
```

Verse 2

```
               D            C              D                C
Jane is in the back yard   doing the outside dance;
D                       C
   I'm telling you the other day
     D                  C
She didn't even get a chance.
              D        C                    D              C
But this is my invitation: a-just-a special vacation;
  D                   C                 D                C
I need your concentration just to,   just to, just to,   just to…
```

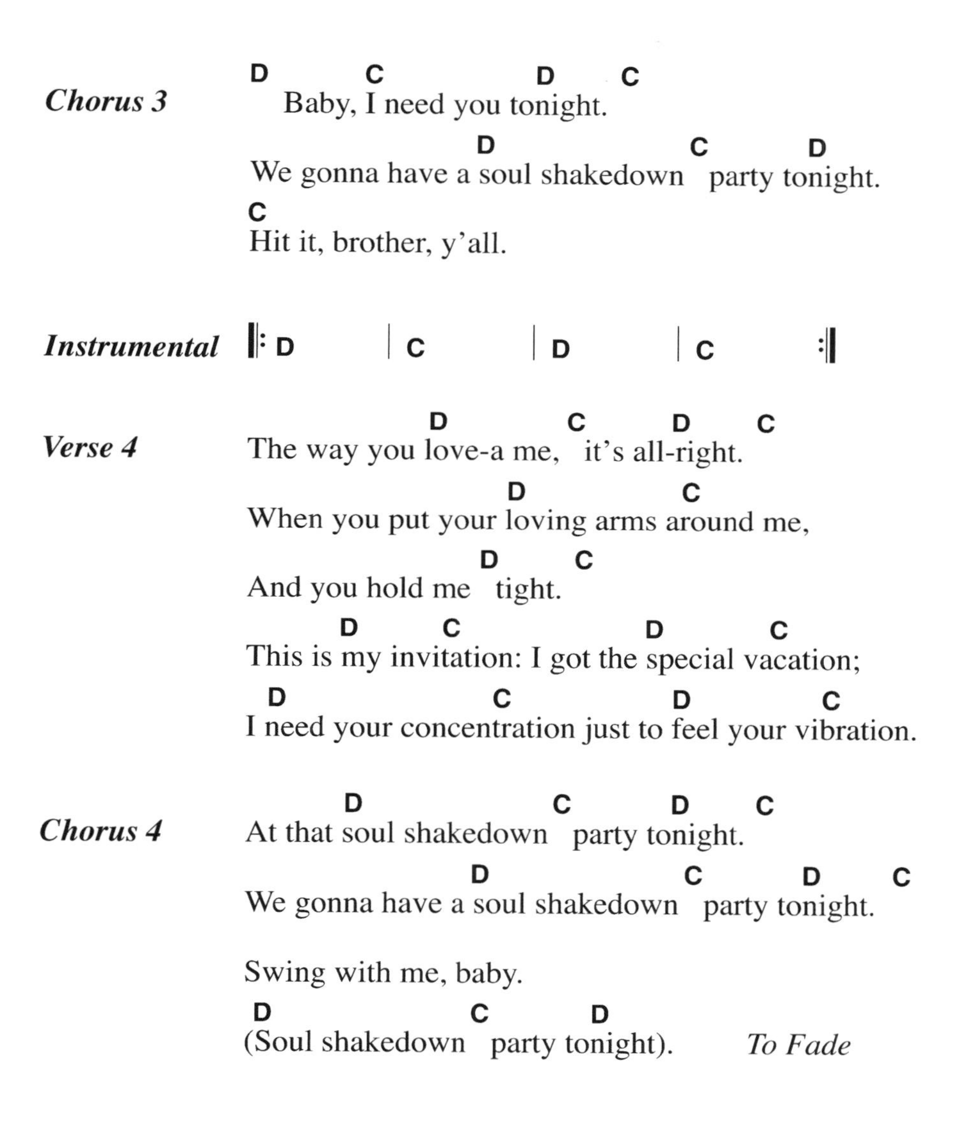

Chorus 3

D C D C
Baby, I need you tonight.

D C D
We gonna have a soul shakedown party tonight.

C
Hit it, brother, y'all.

Instrumental ‖: D | C | D | C :‖

Verse 4

D C D C
The way you love-a me, it's all-right.

D C
When you put your loving arms around me,

D C
And you hold me tight.

D C D C
This is my invitation: I got the special vacation;

D C D C
I need your concentration just to feel your vibration.

Chorus 4

D C D C
At that soul shakedown party tonight.

D C D C
We gonna have a soul shakedown party tonight.

Swing with me, baby.

D C D
(Soul shakedown party tonight). *To Fade*

Stir It Up

Words & Music by
Bob Marley

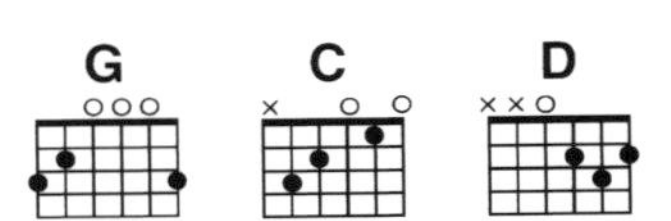

Intro | : G | C D | G | C D : |

Chorus 1

G C D
Stir it up, little darlin',
G C D
Stir it up, c'mon baby, c'mon and
G C D
Stir it up, little darlin'.
G C D
Stir it up.

Verse 1

G
It's been a long, long time
C D G C D
Since I've got you on my mind.
G C D
And now you are here, I said it's so clear,
G C
To see what we could do, baby,
D
Just me and you, come on and

Chorus 2

G C D
Stir it up, little darlin',
G C D
Stir it up, c'mon baby, c'mon and
G C D
Stir it up, little darlin'.
G C D
Stir it up.

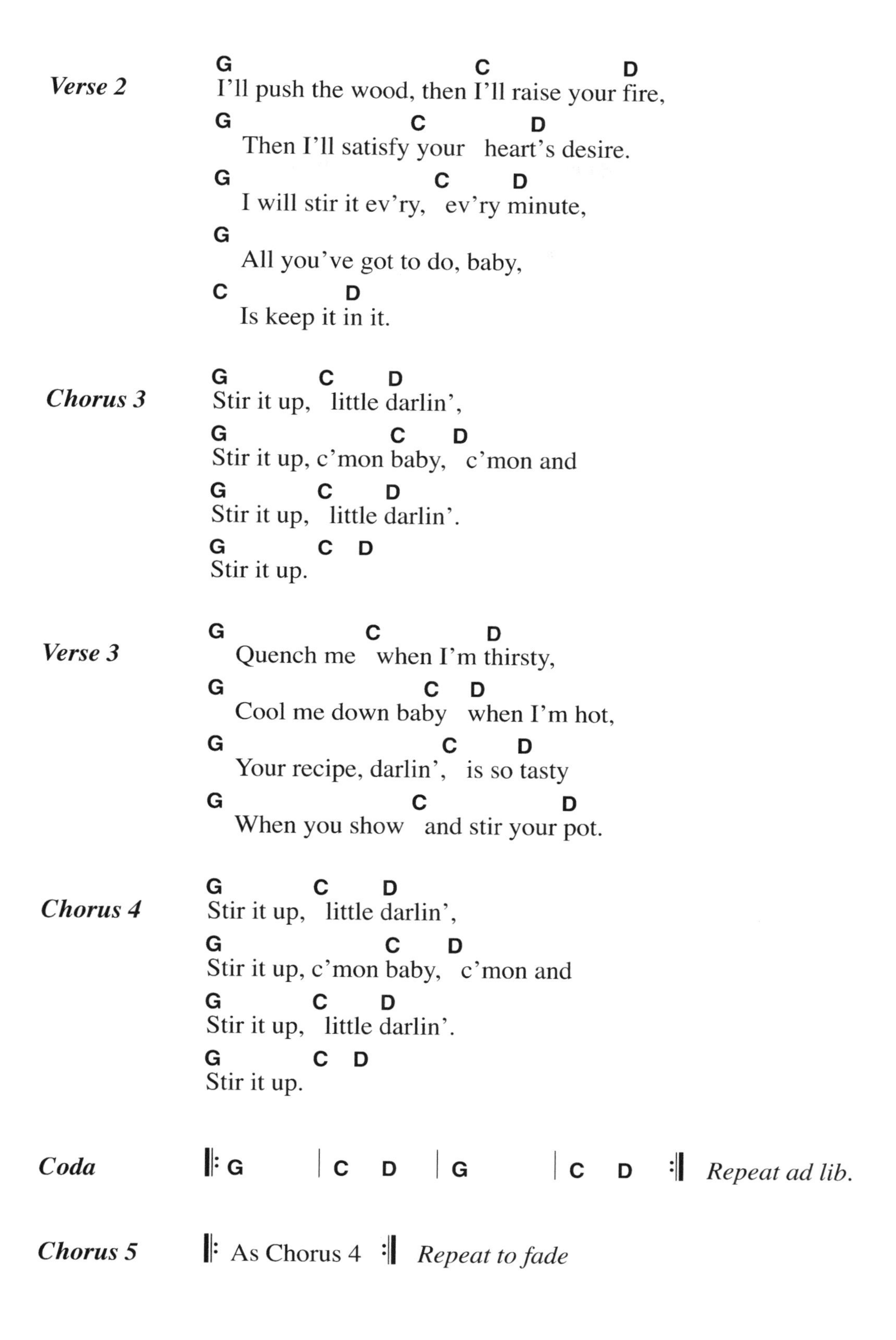

Verse 2

G C D
I'll push the wood, then I'll raise your fire,
G C D
Then I'll satisfy your heart's desire.
G C D
I will stir it ev'ry, ev'ry minute,
G
All you've got to do, baby,
C D
Is keep it in it.

Chorus 3

G C D
Stir it up, little darlin',
G C D
Stir it up, c'mon baby, c'mon and
G C D
Stir it up, little darlin'.
G C D
Stir it up.

Verse 3

G C D
Quench me when I'm thirsty,
G C D
Cool me down baby when I'm hot,
G C D
Your recipe, darlin', is so tasty
G C D
When you show and stir your pot.

Chorus 4

G C D
Stir it up, little darlin',
G C D
Stir it up, c'mon baby, c'mon and
G C D
Stir it up, little darlin'.
G C D
Stir it up.

Coda ‖: G | C D | G | C D :‖ *Repeat ad lib.*

Chorus 5 ‖: As Chorus 4 :‖ *Repeat to fade*

Three Little Birds

Words & Music by
Bob Marley

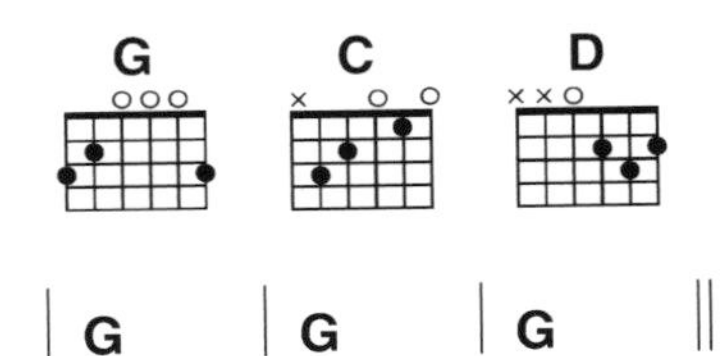

Intro | G | G | G | G ||

```
               G
Chorus 1   Don't worry about a thing,
              C                            G
           'Cos ev'ry little thing gonna be all-right.

           Singin' don't worry about a thing,
              C                            G
           'Cos ev'ry little thing gonna be all-right!

                          G
Verse 1    Rise up this mornin',
                              D
           Smiled with the risin' sun,
                         G
           Three little birds
                          C
           Pitch by my doorstep
                  G
           Singin' sweet songs
                         D
           Of melodies pure and true,
                  C                              G
           Sayin', "This is my message to you-ou-ou:"

                             G
Chorus 2   Singin' don't worry 'bout a thing,
                  C                            G
           'Cause ev'ry little thing gonna be all-right.

           Singin' don't worry (don't worry) 'bout a thing,
              C                            G
           'Cos ev'ry little thing gonna be all-right!
```

Verse 2

```
                G
Rise up this mornin',
                    D
Smiled with the risin' sun,
              G
Three little birds
              C
Pitch by my doorstep
     G
Singin' sweet songs
              D
Of melodies pure and true,
         C                          G
Sayin', "This is my message to you-ou-ou:"
```

Chorus 3

```
                  G
‖: Singin' don't worry about a thing, worry about a thing, oh!
C                                   G
Every little thing gonna be all right, don't worry!

Singin' don't worry about a thing, I won't worry!
         C                                  G
'Cause every little thing gonna be all-right. :‖   Repeat to fade
```

Time Will Tell

Words & Music by
Bob Marley

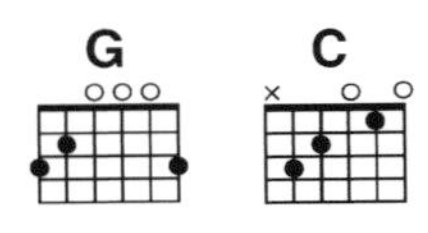

Intro | G C | G C | G C | G C ||

```
            G   C                G                C         G
*Verse 1*       Jah would never give the power to a baldhead,
            C            G     C     G
            Run come crucify the Dread.

            C     G          C        G
*Chorus 1*  Time alone, oh, time will tell:
            C                G                 C          G
            Think you're in heaven, but ya living in hell;
            C                G                 C          G
            Think you're in heaven, but ya living in hell;
            C                G                 C          G
            Think you're in heaven, but ya living in hell.
            C     G          C        G
            Time alone, oh, time will tell.
               C                G                 C          G
            Ya think you're in heaven, but ya living in hell.

            G   C            G      C       G
*Verse 2*       Back them up; oh, not the brothers,
            C   G             C        G
                But the ones   who sets 'em up.

            C     G          C        G
*Chorus 2*  Time alone, oh, time will tell:
            C                G                 C          G
            Think you're in heaven, but ya living in hell;
            C                G                 C          G
            Think you're in heaven, but ya living in hell;
            C                G                 C          G
            Think you're in heaven, but ya living in hell.
```

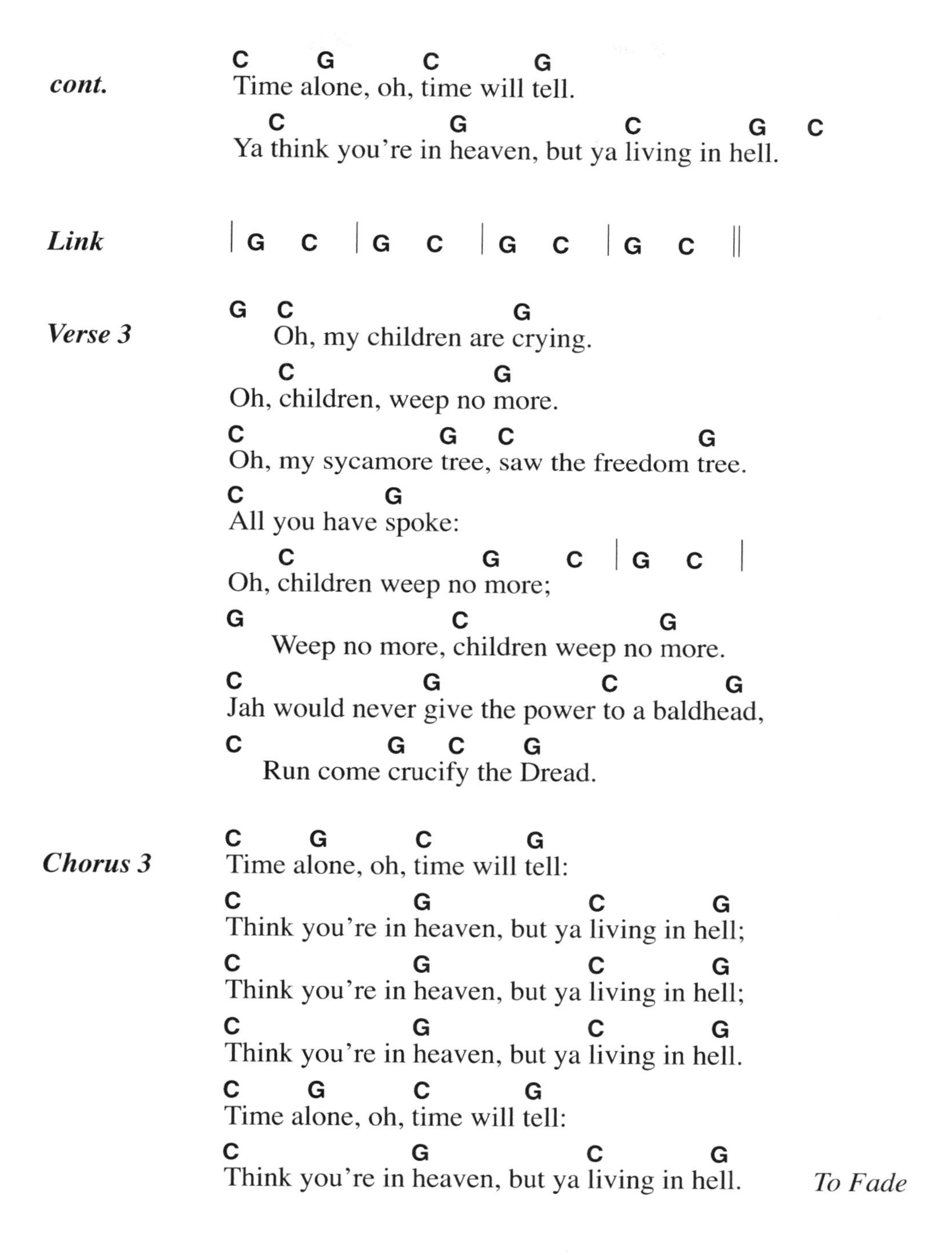

cont.

C G C G
Time alone, oh, time will tell.
C G C G C
Ya think you're in heaven, but ya living in hell.

Link

| G C | G C | G C | G C ||

Verse 3

G C G
Oh, my children are crying.
C G
Oh, children, weep no more.
C G C G
Oh, my sycamore tree, saw the freedom tree.
C G
All you have spoke:
C G C | G C |
Oh, children weep no more;
G C G
Weep no more, children weep no more.
C G C G
Jah would never give the power to a baldhead,
C G C G
Run come crucify the Dread.

Chorus 3

C G C G
Time alone, oh, time will tell:
C G C G
Think you're in heaven, but ya living in hell;
C G C G
Think you're in heaven, but ya living in hell;
C G C G
Think you're in heaven, but ya living in hell.
C G C G
Time alone, oh, time will tell:
C G C G
Think you're in heaven, but ya living in hell. *To Fade*

War

Words & Music by
Allen Cole & Carlton Barrett

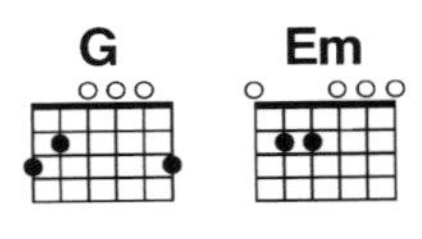

Intro | Em D | Em D ||

Verse 1

```
Em                D                 Em                 D
Until the philosophy which hold one race superior
        Em      D       Em     D    Em      D     Em                D
And another     inferior    is  finally   and permanently
     Em         D      Em
Discredited   and abandoned,
D                       Em    D
   Ev'rywhere is war,
           Em     D
Me say war.
```

Verse 2

```
        Em                D                 Em
That until there're no longer first class
                            D              Em       D
And second class citizens of any nation,
Em                         D
Until the colour of a man's skin
        Em                 D                   Em                  D
Is of no more significance than the colour of his eyes,
           Em     D
Me say war.
```

Verse 3

```
        Em               D
That until the basic human rights
       Em                D
Are equally guaranteed to all,
            Em            D
Without regard to race,
        Em
Dis a war.
```

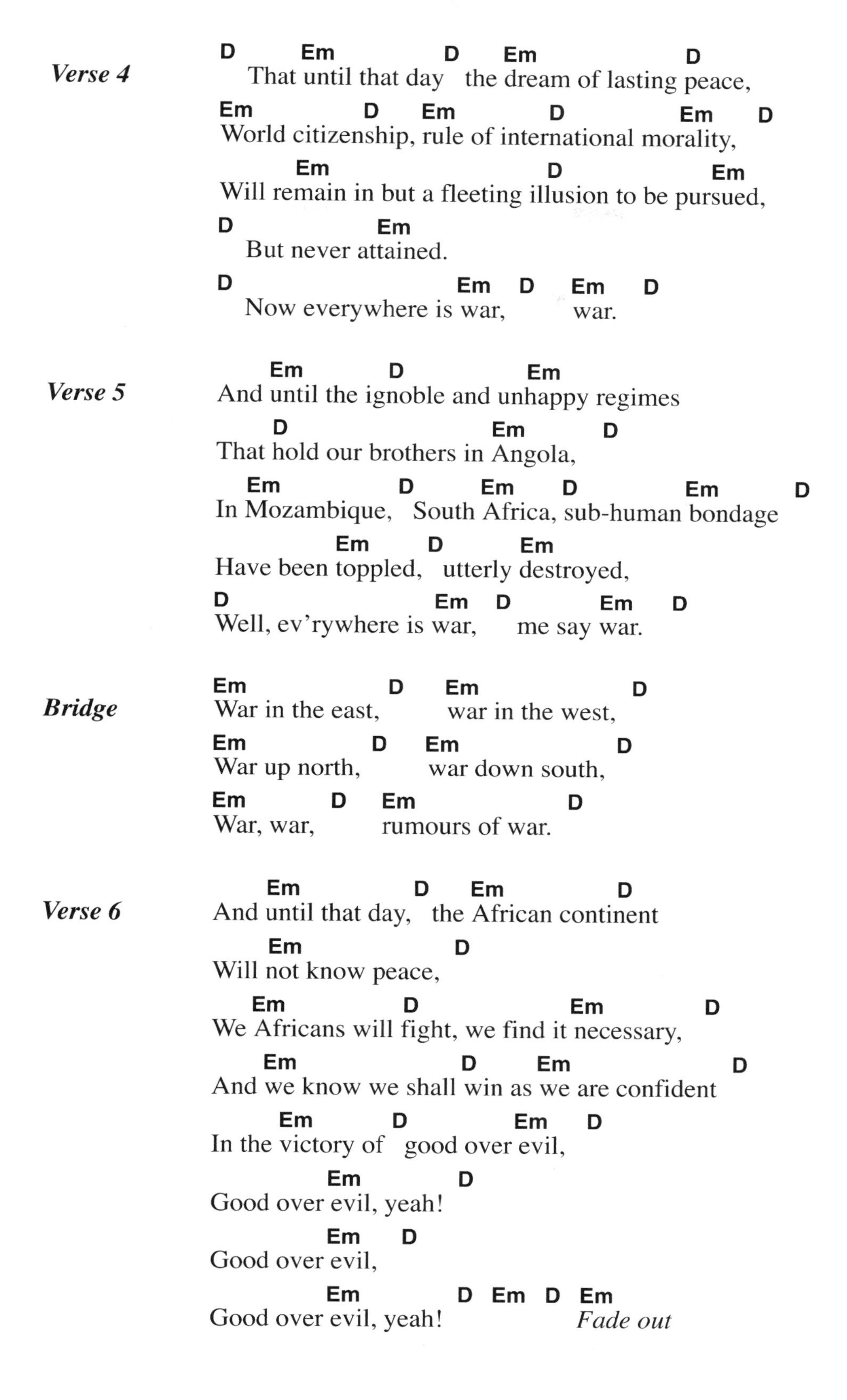

Verse 4

D Em D Em D
That until that day the dream of lasting peace,
Em D Em D Em D
World citizenship, rule of international morality,
Em D Em
Will remain in but a fleeting illusion to be pursued,
D Em
But never attained.
D Em D Em D
Now everywhere is war, war.

Verse 5

Em D Em
And until the ignoble and unhappy regimes
D Em D
That hold our brothers in Angola,
Em D Em D Em D
In Mozambique, South Africa, sub-human bondage
Em D Em
Have been toppled, utterly destroyed,
D Em D Em D
Well, ev'rywhere is war, me say war.

Bridge

Em D Em D
War in the east, war in the west,
Em D Em D
War up north, war down south,
Em D Em D
War, war, rumours of war.

Verse 6

Em D Em D
And until that day, the African continent
Em D
Will not know peace,
Em D Em D
We Africans will fight, we find it necessary,
Em D Em D
And we know we shall win as we are confident
Em D Em D
In the victory of good over evil,
Em D
Good over evil, yeah!
Em D
Good over evil,
Em D Em D Em
Good over evil, yeah! *Fade out*

Relative Tuning

The guitar can be tuned with the aid of pitch pipes or dedicated electronic guitar tuners which are available through your local music dealer. If you do not have a tuning device, you can use relative tuning. Estimate the pitch of the 6th string as near as possible to E or at least a comfortable pitch (not too high, as you might break other strings in tuning up). Then, while checking the various positions on the diagram, place a finger from your left hand on the:

5th fret of the E or 6th string and **tune the open A** (or 5th string) to the note (A)

5th fret of the A or 5th string and **tune the open D** (or 4th string) to the note (D)

5th fret of the D or 4th string and **tune the open G** (or 3rd string) to the note (G)

4th fret of the G or 3rd string and **tune the open B** (or 2nd string) to the note (B)

5th fret of the B or 2nd string and **tune the open E** (or 1st string) to the note (E)

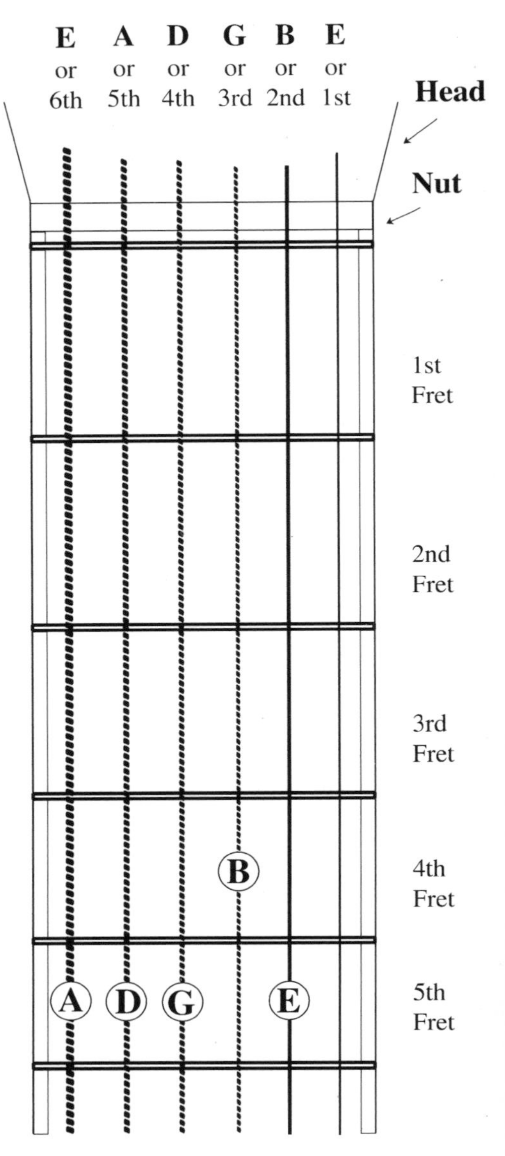

Reading Chord Boxes

Chord boxes are diagrams of the guitar neck viewed head upwards, face on as illustrated. The top horizontal line is the nut, unless a higher fret number is indicated, the others are the frets.

The vertical lines are the strings, starting from E (or 6th) on the left to E (or 1st) on the right.

The black dots indicate where to place your fingers.

Strings marked with an O are played open, not fretted. Strings marked with an X should not be played.

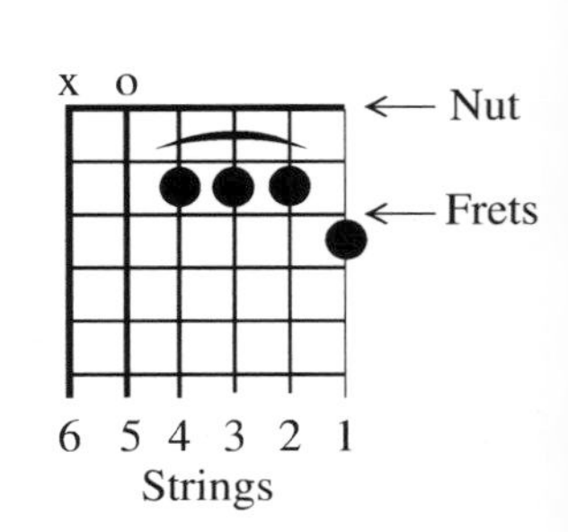